Designing Ship
Sealink

Don Ripley & Tony Rogan

ISBN 1 871947 34 0
Published by

FERRY
Publications

12 Millfields Close, Kilgetty, Pembrokeshire, SA68 0SA Tel: 01834 813991 Fax: 01834 814484

CONTENTS

Editor: John Hendy
Design: Miles Cowsill

Earl Granville (FotoFlite)

FOREWORD

As Rolls and Royce became synonymous with the prestige motor car so too have the names Rogan and Ripley in the context of the design of the modern multi-purpose roll on/roll off ship.

I first heard of Tony Rogan and Don Ripley, Naval Architects, when I accepted the task of contributing to the marketing of the shipping services of British Rail Scottish Region in 1967. At that time BR Scotland owned and operated the shipping fleets trading under the name of the Caledonian Steam Packet Company providing passenger car and freight services across the River Clyde and to and from the Highland and Island communities of the West Coast of Scotland. BR Scotland also owned and operated the Stranraer-Larne service later to become British Transport Ship Management (Scotland) Limited and the delightful paddle steamer the *Maid of the Loch* which cruised around the 'bonnie banks' of Loch Lomond.

In 1968 I took the "high road (or was it the low road?)" and joined Tony and Don in London where we worked in the headquarters of the newly-formed British Rail Shipping and International Services Division. The SISD, as it is known, was staffed by the elite group of the railway community (at least they told me they were elite!). This group was responsible for making the rail and sea services from the UK, Republic of Ireland and the Channel Islands connect with the rail networks of Continental Europe. The same group could sit down happily in the evenings and enjoy reading Cook's International Timetable – then that was because they wrote it (well almost!).

The SISD was part of a consortium or partnership with the Zeeland shipping company, SNCF shipping services and The Belgian Marine Authority. Collectively they operated 82 ships (plus tugs and dredgers) on 19 routes – surely the world's largest ferry company? SISD also owned or leased 11 ports or terminals.

Such was the marine portfolio of the consortium's naval architects – the biggest part of the consortium fleet became the responsibility of Tony Rogan and Don Ripley. Train ferries, estuarial craft, classic passenger ships, conventional multi-purpose ferries, dedicated cargo ships, container ships, overnight passenger/car/freight ships – all to be maintained, modified, converted or built from scratch. All with differing configurations, all designed to the highest standards of safety demanded by the international marine authorities, all required to satisfy the ever-changing needs of the passenger and freight transport markets of Europe.

This book describes the new-builds and conversions designed by Tony and Don between 1954 and 1992 and takes the reader through the

Jim Hannah

period of British Rail Administration, including the run-up to privatisation and the creation of the brand name – SEALINK (destined to vanish on 1 January 1996) also taking in the period of ownership by Sea Containers and the initial period of Stena Line ownership.

We are fortunate that Tony and Don can now share with us the technical and commercial innovations which influence the design development of the Sealink fleet. Their remarkable contribution to this development is endorsed by the continuing performance and versatility of the modern ro/ro ferries in service today.

There can be no better examples of the level of their achievement as naval architects than the 'Saint class' ships built in the early 80's in Belfast and at present actively engaged in the Stena UK fleet.

Hats off lads to the *St David*, *St Christopher* and *St Anselm* – or whatever name they sail under now. To the enthusiast they will always be known as the 'Saint class ships'.

If you are interested in the design evolution of the modern ferry you will enjoy sharing the experiences of Tony Rogan and Don Ripley, Naval Architects.

My sincere thanks to Stena Line and to Miles Cowsill and John Hendy of Ferry Publications for their assistance in publishing 'Designing Ships for Sealink'.

J A Hannah
September 1995

THE AUTHORS

Donald Ripley was born in Doncaster in 1927. He started his long career in ship design when at the age of sixteen he became an apprentice draughtsman at the Richard Dunston Shipyard at Thorne. In 1954 he joined British Railways Irish Shipping Services at Euston as assistant chief draughtsman, two years later moving to the newly established ship design office at the British Transport Commission. The formation of the Shipping Division in 1968 saw the department move to Liverpool Street and when Sealink U.K. Ltd. was finally denationalised in 1984, it was absorbed by Sea Containers' naval architects, Hart Fenton Ltd.

Between 1967 and 1992, Don worked with the U.K. Chamber of Shipping and the DOT on background committee work on new Regulations while attending IMO meetings as a member of UK Delegation. More recently he has become the Associate Editor of the RINA quarterly journal, 'Shiprepair & Conversion Technology.'

He was a City Councillor in his home town of St. Albans from 1968 – 73.

Don lists cricket, reading and golf as his interests.

Tony Rogan was born in 1929, close to the Vickers-Armstrong shipyard where he served a shipbuilding apprenticeship from 1945 to 1950. After graduating with honours in Applied Science (Naval Architecture) from the University of Durham he was, for two years, a National Service Sub-Lieutenant (E) mostly watchkeeping at sea following training at the Royal Naval Engineering College. He was then appointed Ship Surveyor to Lloyd's Register of Shipping, from 1955 to 1960, with experience in new-building and ship-repair yards, also in ship research and plan approval.

In 1960, Tony joined the British Rail Shipping and International Services Department where he served as Principal Naval Architect with prime responsibility for new-buildings and major conversions until privatisation. After the acquisition of Sealink UK Ltd by Sea Containers, Tony took his team of Naval Architects to Hart Fenton (a subsidiary of Sea Containers) joining as a Director in 1984. Most of the next ten years to retirement were devoted to Sealink design work. Until retirement Tony was Chairman of the UK Chamber of Shipping construction Committee and a member of Lloyd's Register of Shipping's Technical Committee, he is also a past Chairman of Council and a past President of the London Branch of the RINA.

Tony lists bridge, watercolour painting and learning to play the piano as his interests.

Sea Freightliner II (Jim Ashby collection)

PREFACE

The retirement of Tony Rogan early in 1994 saw the end of a unique double act in ship design. Tony Rogan as Principal Naval Architect and Don Ripley as his Deputy, who had retired a year before, were between them associated with the design and building of a remarkable number of ships for over 30 years (see appendix for the full list).

Don started in the old Irish Shipping Services in 1954 and cut his teeth on the three new Heysham/Belfast steamers just about to be ordered from Harland's and Denny's.

Tony joined the Shipping & International Services Department in 1960 and together they put together a huge dossier of ships with wide ranging variety in size and type, from tugs to hopper barges, from river ferries to estuarial car carriers, train ferries to high class passenger and vehicle ferries.

When the Shipping & International Services Division was formed the existing department was joined by the marine departments of the Southern Region, Eastern Region and the Irish Shipping Services and brought together under the one roof at Liverpool Street Station and began working together instead of competing rivals. The technical personnel were quickly knitted into a coherent team.

Tony Rogan, Principal Naval Architect, was responsible for the design and production of all new ships and for major conversions. David Barwell, Supt. Marine Engineer in Chief, was responsible for the maintenance of the fleet and responsible under Tony Rogan for the selection of machinery for new ships and its installation. Bob Sherwood was the Chief Marine Supt. responsible for the safe operation of the fleet.

Under the direction of Tony Rogan, the relationship between the design team and the port and seagoing staff took on a new and open form. Previously they had not been allowed to discuss any aspect of new ships or modifications directly with the port staff and had in fact to carry out all exchanges by letter up and down the chains of command. Under the new order open discussions took place in the port before the specification was finalised for a new project and all were invited to contribute – it took a little time to sink in but was then highly rewarding. Suggestions came in thick and fast and were all responded to. The port staff and ships crews felt that they had made some contribution to the new ships and they were correct. Many suggestions and ideas were incorporated and better ships resulted.

It was a pleasure to build ships when we had wholehearted co-operation of such captains as Monty Grigor in Harwich, John Arthur and Tom Manton in Dover, John Toogood in Newhaven, Len Evans in Holyhead and Bob Bathgate in Stranraer. They knew their ships from truck to keel and brought enthusiasm for new projects to their crews.

Tony also started the technical conferences between the U.K., French, Dutch and Belgian partners in the Sealink operation and over a couple of days once or twice each year new ideas, progress on problems and updating on new projects were freely exchanged.

With the expansion of the vehicle carrying facilities it was important that ships could use a number of ports and flexibility was the 'in' word when new designs were considered.

Caledonian Princess (John Hendy)

INTRODUCTION

The design of any ship is a complex process, a mixture of art and science, and a process in which many compromises are necessary to achieve, within the confines of a floating body, the many objectives set in terms of commercial requirements, operational performance, and safety and classification society rules and regulations.

A cross-Channel ferry is one of the more complex types of merchant ship, demands on space and weight, in particular, being a constant concern to the designer. The naval architect is constrained by berthing limitations on the dimensions of the ship in designing ferries capable of operating, at all states of the tide, in harbours often created to take advantage of the shortest possible sea crossings.

The Authors have been privileged, in a partnership of over a third of a century, to have been involved in the design, construction, and equipping of a wide variety of short-sea and estuarial ships, 'classic' passenger ferries, passenger and vehicle ferries, train ferries, and cellular container ships. Their careers span, among other things, the development of the Ro-Ro concept almost from the beginning to the present day 'state-of-the-art'.

Working within the framework of a nationalised industry, design was frequently compromised by investment limitations, threats of a Channel Tunnel, and perhaps, most of all, by the inherent inertia of the railways establishment.

Sealink overcame these inhibitions to compete on level terms with private enterprise, be profitable, and to offer, at the time of privatisation, a viable concern to bidders.

What follows is intended to set out not only a factual account of the acquisition of the 'hardware' for the Sealink Fleet, but also to record much of the background to the building of that fleet, sometimes anecdotal, sometimes expressing the designers' experiences and frustrations in things that might have happened, and in some cases reporting things that did not quite go according to plan.

This book is dedicated to the many people: colleagues in Sealink, shipyards, national administrations and classification societies, hydrodynamic laboratories, subcontractors and suppliers of equipment and materials, who have all contributed to the designs for which the Authors have been responsible, and not least to our wives.

We should also mention that as a nationalised company it was incumbent on the designers of ships for Sealink to be totally up-to-date with the U.K. Statutory Requirements, and ensure that the ships were always in compliance with the spirit of the latest regulations. This involved attending many meetings with U K Authorities, and participating with them in the evolution of regulations in the international forum, The International Maritime Organisation, where our experience over the building of many passenger vessels enabled us to contribute a practical aspect to rule making, and enable some modifications to be included in IMO proposals.

Ailsa Princess (Miles Cowsill)

CARTOON

An enlarged and framed copy of this cartoon was taken from an old edition of 'Shipbuilding & Shipping Record', and hung successively in Ted Dewdney's, then Tony's and then Don's office. It was brought out on occasions when we had what we thought were conflicting ideas put forward at some of those interminable 'planning' meetings. It usually stopped the show, as the message quickly got through.

THE TEAM

From an initial naval architect's team of three, plus one marine engineer, the Shipping & International Services Division's Naval Architect's Department expanded, in 1970, to its maximum of seven. The following memorandum, an annual report from Tony to the Shipping Division Board, outlines the responsibilities, organisation, and activities of the department.

MEMORANDUM TO THE GENERAL MANAGER

REPORT FROM THE PRINCIPAL NAVAL
ARCHITECT
SHIPPING & INTERNATIONAL SERVICES
DIVISION

INTRODUCTION

1.The objects of this report are to comment upon -
a) The functional responsibilities of the Principal Naval Architect.
b) The organisation required to fulfil these responsibilities.
c) The implementation of the Board's new construction plans.
d) Technical developments.

FUNCTIONAL RESPONSIBILITIES

2. The primary responsibilities of the Principal Naval Architect are to give advice and cost estimates in the planning stages of new projects; prepare designs and specifications for new ships and major conversions or modifications; take the lead in co-operation with the Supplies Manager in the selection of tenderers, negotiations with contractors and in recommending acceptance of tenders; develop designs with successful shipbuilders including approval of drawings and specifications; oversee the construction of new tonnage and accept new ships after completion of trials.
3. These responsibilities in the new Division are little changed from those in the Shipping and International Services Department organisation where the Board H.Q. reserved to itself, amongst other things, responsibility for the construction of new ships.

"That's right! - Approve the design, then come to me when it's finished and say you want one end pointed-"

4. Further responsibilities include professional advice to Management within the Principal Naval Architect's specialisation, particularly on matters affecting safety of life at sea and seaworthiness. The Principal Naval Architect also co-operates with the Chief Marine Superintendent, the Engineering Superintendent in Chief and the Passenger Services Manager in respect of existing ships. In this latter role he acts virtually as a consultant to his colleagues.

5. Liaison with outside bodies involves close contact and committee work with the Board of Trade, Chamber of Shipping, the Shipping Federation, British Ship Research Association, etc., and from time to time includes attendance with U.K. delegations at IMCO Conferences.

ORGANISATION

6. The small staff shown below is employed at Liverpool Street Headquarters in the work listed above, the greater part of this staff's time being devoted to new construction. Close co-operation is maintained with the other professional officers, particularly the Superintendent Engineer in Chief, one of whose officers is engaged solely in new construction.

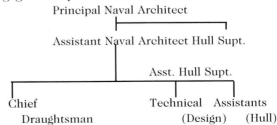

Under the supervision of the Assistant Naval Architect, the office staff prepare estimates, design drawings, calculations and specifications and vet for approval many hundreds of shipyard drawings and specifications each year.

The Hull Superintendent and his assistant (about to be appointed) are practical shipbuilders who are responsible for ensuring that contractors comply with the Board's specifications and that materials and workmanship used in construction are satisfactory.

The Principal Naval Architect and his Assistant also pay regular visits to shipyards to monitor progress and for discussions with the Builders.

IMPLEMENTATION OF BOARD'S NEW CONSTRUCTION PLANS

7. Much thought has been given to the immediate future, to the technical resources required to implement the long term plan and to such problems as berth availability in shipyards, probable delivery dates achievable etc.

8. The level of work in recent times has been such that existing staff has been fully stretched in dealing with work in hand to the value of £5 to 7 1/2 million (i.e. on average of three new ships plus conversions). Work in hand at the present time amounts to some £5 1/2 million (i.e. three new ships plus 2 major conversions).

9. Currently, design work is in hand for five new ships (three designs) and it is likely that within one year work to the value of between £15 and £18 million will be in hand. A modest increase in staff will shortly be proposed to deal with the expected increased work load and to cope with geographical extension of resources involved in building abroad.

10. Whilst the Division's forward planning anticipates required new building for the next five years, concern is felt in regard to the availability of building berths both in U.K. and abroad. Thinking in the last ten years has been geared to ship construction times of 18 months from order to completion. Most shipyards now have order books extending well into 1972 and beyond and vacant berths are rapidly filling up. Construction periods in the order of 2 1/2 years must be anticipated in the immediate future and forward planning adjusted to meet this situation.

11. The buoyant situation in shipyards together with extended delivery dates has also had a marked effect on shipbuilding prices. Following the "buyers market" of recent years, the trend of costs is illustrated in the table below:-

Ship	Ordered	Cost £m
Maid of Kent	1957	1.67
Caledonian Princess	1959	1.85
Holyhead Ferry I	1964	1.63
Antrim Princess	1966	2.00
Vortigern	1968	2.40
New Stranraer Ship	1969	2.65 (Italy)
		2.85 (Lowest U.K. price)

It is of interest that the price quoted for the new Stranraer ship by the builders of the *Antrim*

Sarnia and **Maid of Kent** *(Ferry Publications Library)*

Princess was some 45% higher than the cost of the sister ship ordered three years earlier.

TECHNICAL DEVELOPMENTS

12. New standards, equipment and concepts are continually being incorporated in the Board's new ships. The process of evolution is a continuous one and it is not often that fundamental changes (e.g. to cellular container ships) are necessary. The development of roll-on/roll-off is perhaps the easiest discernable trend and this trend is to be continued in our latest multi-purpose designs.

Improved standards of passenger accommodation are proposed in the new ships now planned. The achievement of these higher standards, involving provision of greater areas of public room space, at a time when statutory safety requirements are becoming more onerous, will not be easy.

13. Safety aspects of the vehicle type ferry are currently being investigated at IMCO level, and the Division is co-operating with the B.O.T. in this work. It is too early to comment on this work which could well have a significant effect upon the future design and operation of this type of ship.

14. Developments in new fields, e.g. push-barge operation, multi-hulled ships etc., are being followed closely.

A. J. ROGAN
PRINCIPAL NAVAL ARCHITECT

Countersigned

Submitted by J. L. HARRINGTON
GENERAL MANAGER

Shipping & International Services Division
Ref. MD.4994/87
15th December, 1969

This memorandum is from an exciting time when, despite having to cope with an exacting programme of ship design, supervision of construction, and the major conversion of a number of ferries, we were involved in investigations of several novel and innovative concepts from grass roots levels. How we managed to encompass so many widely different activities is now difficult to comprehend.

Whilst each member of the team had particular areas of expertise, a considerable degree of flexibility was essential to cope with a varied work load.

Project Managers Eddie Robson, Dan Watson and later Eddy Geddes were all capable of preparation of design work, calculations, specifications, drawings and also the eventual physical inspection and supervision of work in shipyards and ship repair yards. Fred Crossby,

who originally joined the team to project manage interior outfit work from a shop-fitting background, became our in-house interior designer but also quickly acquired the skills of practical shipbuilding. Tony Dickinson, an exceptionally skilled naval architect, had the responsibility for making Tony and Don's ideas really work. He was a numbers man who could be relied upon to accurately estimate weights and centres of gravity, design lines and satisfy stability and safety criteria, calculate speed and horsepower requirements, all essential to design performance. But occasionally even he had to abandon his computing to Project Manage major shipyard contracts. We suspect that while he sometimes enjoyed getting his hands dirty, he was always happy to return to his real love: pure naval architecture.

Bert Cockett, a legend in his time and a key member of the team, sadly died as we were completing a four ship contract with the shipyard where he was trained – Harland & Wolff. There was never a more dedicated and competent Superintendent and he made his mark in every shipyard where we built, at home and abroad, and is remembered with great affection. Tales of his necessary confrontations with shipyard managers, to achieve the standards upon which he insisted, would fill another book. Without exception, they all were happy to acknowledge that they benefited from his unequalled expertise in ferry construction.

The dedication of both our team and of our Sealink colleagues was complete, with no regard for working hours or days off. Nobody ever decided to leave us! Perhaps the reason was that we were all 'hooked' on ferry design. Don was once severely reprimanded by the Deputy Managing Director at a staff appraisal interview for saying that he obtained so much job satisfaction that, if he could afford it, he would be "quite happy to work for nothing." He was told firmly not to express such views in public as they would not help him when salary rises were being considered!

DESIGN

Merchant ship design commences with the identification of a commercial requirement for new tonnage. This requirement will normally be initiated by one or more of the following:-

i) replacement of life-expired units

ii) need for additional or larger ships to meet increased traffic demands

iii) establishment of new routes

iv) technological advances providing new commercial opportunities.

There are examples of each of these in this record of development of the Sealink fleet. In addition to new ship construction, the continuous update of existing ships by way of major conversions is of interest.

In Sealink, the first step in identifying future requirements was the maintenance of a running long term investment plan to which all senior management contributed. Having made a pitch, on an annual basis, for a share of the Treasury controlled British Rail budget, Sealink were inevitably required to trim their investment proposals in most years. Nevertheless the long term plan identified a constant stream of newbuilding and conversion projects for which Sealink's small Naval Architects' Department had prime responsibility for implementing from first ideas to completion.

Initial commercial requirements were usually broadly based, needing in most cases, a technical study of several alternative proposals. For some projects a comprehensive operational research exercise was necessary in which alternative sizes, capacities and speeds of ships were examined, sometimes alternative routes, and even alternative ship types were investigated. In these early stages, outline design ideas were formulated and shot estimates made of first costs, together with information to enable operating costs to be calculated. These exercises were essentially computations based on simplified ship geometries which provided the Planning Department of Sealink with numbers required initially for the Long Term Plan, and eventually with the information required for the detailed financial case to justify the selected design option.

The detailed financial case for a new project always had to surmount a number of hurdles in the approval process, viz : Sealink Management Committee,(or in earlier years the Shipping and International Services Committee), a full British Railways Board, and the Department of Transport, all within limits set by the Treasury. The amount of time consumed in these procedures was frustrating and inhibiting. They did, however, provide a breathing space in organising design activities ! There was rarely any doubt that preparing designs and contract documents would take no longer than financial investment approvals.

The development of basic commercial design requirements into drawings and specifications suitable for competitive tendering from shipyards was a process in which much consultation was necessary. First discussions were between the Naval Architects Department and those of the Commercial, Marine Engineering, Marine Superintendents, and Passenger Services/Catering Departments. Preliminary designs were agreed with the heads of these departments, usually after preparing numerous 'Aunt Sally' ideas. Interior Design Architects were invited to become involved the moment a basic ship geometry was agreed, so that they could develop their schemes with minimum restraint, and before too much was 'cast in concrete'. Later consultation processes involved ships' crews, port staff and unions, initially in correspondence, and eventually with meetings for open discussion with ships' officers, crew, port staff and unions. In all, several hundred people were given the opportunity to comment on designs before orders were placed. This consultation procedure produced numerous headaches for the naval architects, but without doubt was beneficial in picking the brains of those who operated the ships and could give valuable feedback on past errors and omissions.

Few laymen have an understanding of the juggling acts naval architects must perform in the design of a ship, particularly a ferry which is confined in dimensions, must be relatively light in weight, stable both when intact and when damaged, capable of performing with guaranteed reliability in all weathers and, most importantly, provide passenger and vehicle spaces which will attract the customer in a highly competitive field. When assessing the demands of operating and commercial departments (who had no responsibility for eventual capital cost of a new ship) it was always reasonable to assume that, if they were provided with everything in a new project that they initially requested, the resulting design would be grossly uneconomic and would never be built ! Delicate negotiations with colleagues was then an important preliminary stage in the process leading to a finalised design.

Particularly close relationships were necessary with our marine engineering and marine counterparts. The latter's expertise was essential to the establishment of fundamental ship dimensions, and to agreement on many operational aspects of design, particularly speed, navigation and manoeuvrability. The Marine

Cambridge Ferry (FotoFlite)

Engineering department, including electrics/electronics, were more intimately involved in machinery space design and specification, and were effectively a part of the design/ construction team from start to finish of projects.

The multitudinous sets of Rules and Regulations with which ships, particularly passenger ships, must comply constrain the designer, sometimes in ways not easily comprehended by non-technical colleagues. For instance the layout of a passenger ferry below the main vehicle deck (main subdivision deck) is determined by considerations of watertight subdivision, (usually assuming damage to and flooding of two adjacent compartments) and taking into account the effect on stability (ability to remain stable and upright) of the assumed damage. Similarly the requirements for structural fire protection have a significant effect on the layout of passenger spaces in the higher areas of the ship. The appointed interior design architect must be fully aware of, and able to cope with, the difficult restrictions placed on him by the Rules and Regulations in meeting what, for him, is essentially a commercial remit.

For most of the period covered by this book, both the Naval Architects' department and the appointed interior design architect, who was effectively a part of the naval architects' team, were required to respond to the British Railways Board Design Panel, and to obtain the Panel's approval to all aspects of ship design discernible to the public, the customer. Design approval for interior spaces was based on submission of schematic drawings, colour schemes, materials selections, and perspective pictorial representations of proposals. The Design Panel

was comprised of eminent experts in the field of design including, from the shipping world, Sir Colin Anderson. The relationship with the Board's Design Officers, George Williams and Jim Cousins, was always positive and fruitful. An example of the value of this was the successful introduction of a corporate identity manual covering every visual aspect from exterior painting and funnel logo schemes to lettering details of interior signs and notices.

The Interior Design Architect, appointed, up to privatisation, by the British Railways Board Design Panel, but nevertheless an integral part of the naval architects' team, was responsible for meeting the commercial passenger remit, including visible service areas, within the cost, and the space and technical limitations defined by the naval architects department, which was eventually responsible for the final outcome. Practice was to separate passenger areas from the rest of the ship in shipbuilding contracts. Precise demarcation of responsibilities, practical and financial, ensured that complete control was exercised in achieving the desired standard of finish.

For 25 years, from the *Maid of Kent* to the *St. Helen*, Ward and Austin, later Ward Associates, were appointed interior design architects to the Sealink fleet. Their work encompassed not only all new ships (excluding the *Caesarea*) but also many major passenger ship conversions. Ships are quite different to 'land based' projects and are subject to restrictions and limitations foreign to the uninitiated. Ward and Austin quickly developed webbed feet and became acclaimed leaders in their field in the U.K., hence Neville Ward's award of Royal Designer to Industry. Progress in providing passengers with an ambience and level of comfort appropriate to modern expectations was, however, retarded by a misguided view that all visible surfaces should be easily maintained, i.e. capable of being wiped down with a damp cloth ! Hard surfaces, vinyl seat covers, PVC floors, and plastic laminate linings thus persisted almost until privatisation, much to the frustration of both interior designers and naval architects.

A 'breath of fresh air', after privatisation, was the declared intention of Jim Sherwood, President of Sea Containers, to shake off what he regarded as the jaded image of the previously nationalised fleet by improving passenger comfort. This enthusiasm was, no doubt, fired by the imminent arrival of competition from the Channel Tunnel.

Sea Containers' initial enthusiasm for investment in improvement in standards resulted in the employment of numerous interior design architects, often without ship experience, but always with great dedication. Early results were mixed, sometimes brilliant interior designs on services doomed to failure, others, mediocre designs on services guaranteed to survive. Perhaps the apogee of the Sea Containers' policy were the conversions of the *Fantasia* and *Fiesta* which set new standards in cross-Channel passenger comfort, capable of competing effectively with the Channel Tunnel.

RAILWAY SHIPPING

The operation of ships by the Railway Companies has a long and interesting history. The mid to late Victorian expansion of the railway network to the coastal ports resulted in the railway companies entering the field of ship owning. It was considered essential to the procuring and retention of passenger custom that the passenger should be able to continue on a 'through' basis to the opposite railhead when reaching the coast and that there should be a shipping connection to minimise delays. To ensure this, the railway companies built their own ships to fit the particular requirement of their routes. Thus, almost by accident, occurred the biggest ever impetus to the evolution of the cross-Channel packets as they were then called.

Mail contracts were also competed for by the railway companies, usually on the basis of the fastest through journey, including the sea voyage, and passenger comfort was often a very secondary consideration when speed was a prerequisite of obtaining a contract from The Royal Mail and this continued right up to the 2nd World War.

As an interesting aside it is entertaining to look back on the variety of the services at the turn of the century.

The 1902 Baedeker Guide for London gives the following list of routes from England to the Continent:-

Dover – Calais
Dover – Ostend
Folkestone – Boulogne
Queenborough – Flushing (Vlissingen)
Newhaven – Dieppe
Harwich – Hook of Holland
Harwich – Antwerp
Tilbury – Calais
London – Rotterdam
Harwich – Hamburg
Harwich – Esbjerg
London – Gothenburg
London – Kristiansand
London – Bremen
Southampton – Bremen
Plymouth – Cuxhaven
Southampton – Cherbourg
Southampton – Le Havre
London – Bordeaux
Newhaven – Caen
Southampton – Caen
Newhaven – Trouville
Southampton – Trouville
Southampton – St. Malo.

The nationalisation of the former railway companies in 1948 took place in the midst of the post-war programme of ferry building to replace those lost during the war and to assist in the expansion of services in the late 1940's and early 1950's.

Those ships were designed by the shipyard naval architects to a brief specification of requirements and performance prepared by the Owners, usually giving a guaranteed time between ports, which at that time was the vital element. The designs used were very largely those put on hold in 1939 when the normal programme of tonnage replacement was suspended.

A second surge in design came in the early 1960's when the car carrying capability of ferries began to expand rapidly and the size of ferries grew accordingly.

With the growth in size came improvement in comfort, all the ferries were then being fitted with fin stabilisers, and the reduction in movement was further illustrated by the stopping of the securing of cars. All commercial vehicles were secured to the deck but we no longer fitted the tie-down wires along the car decks and terminated the supply of rope ties.

Another development was the supply to the ships of shorter securing chains for commercial vehicles. We had started to notice that chains, then specified at 10 feet long, were disappearing from the vehicle decks in increasing numbers. Checks were made and it was discovered that lorry drivers had decided that a 10ft. chain, capable of holding a Ro-Ro vehicle in position in rough weather, made a good towing chain. We decreased the distance between securing points

St George (FotoFlite)

and specified chains of only 7'6". This brought an abrupt end of problem as the new chains were too short to use for towing.

A structural problem in the early days of all-welded ships was cracking of the shell plating in way of the propellers. The cracks sometimes ran down one side, sometimes both, of the frames in line with the thrust of water from the blades. With the use of toe-welded angles in lieu of riveted-on flanges, the effective span between frames had been increased by as much as 12% and to remedy this we increased the shell thickness to compensate. The *Caledonian Princess* and *Antrim Princess* were prime examples, probably affected by the shallow water in Loch Ryan.

Don Ripley joined the railways shipping section in March 1954 and was appointed as assistant to the Chief Draughtsman in the Irish Shipping Services in the old Euston Station. The Department was the collective headquarters of the shipping interests of the London Midland, Western and Scottish Regions covering services from Fishguard, Holyhead, Heysham, Stranraer, Lake Windermere, Tilbury/Gravesend, Dartmouth/Kingswear ferries and Plymouth tenders.

The Manager was Capt. John Dudley Reid, Supt. Engineer Mr. Thomas Copland and the Marine Supt. was Capt. Robert Sherwood. Among the Department's responsibilities were the marine workshops and dry docks in Holyhead where a full programme of annual refits and ship repair filled the calendar and provided the principal employment for the Welsh port.

All the west coast ships were docked in Holyhead for underwater survey but a considerable proportion of floating survey work was carried out in Fishguard and Heysham by the local marine workshop staff on the ships based at those two ports.

As far as he could ascertain Don was the first technical employee in any of the railway services who had been trained in a shipyard and this was to be of value to him in the expanding world of railway ships after 1954.

One of the first tasks he was given was to study the official report of the loss of the Stranraer ferry *Princess Victoria* in the great storm of January 1953. It was still a major topic of discussion in 1954 and was the cause of wide-ranging changes in the shipping departments of the Railway Regions and eventually led to the setting up of the Shipping and International Services Department at British Transport Commission Headquarters at Marylebone in 1956, of which more later.

Don's own feeling after reading the Report, and listening to the comments of older colleagues who knew those involved, was that the ship's Master, Captain James Ferguson, must have been totally convinced that his ship would ride out the storm, or otherwise he would have tried run it ashore. One practical result of the tragedy was the decision not to build any further passenger ships with open sterns. The practice in those days was to sail in any weather, even if many of the passengers would have preferred a delay of some hours. Don remembers being on the bridge of one of the older 'Dukes' leaving Heysham one night with heavy rain and snow being driven horizontally by a westerly gale, and the Captain conning the ship with great difficulty from the open bridge wing, having a second officer at the wheelhouse door to relay his orders to the seaman on the telegraph, and the rudimentary radar blinking away in the corner, mistrusted by one and all. A foul trip that was not enjoyed by a single person on board.

NEWBUILDS

D.I. Harmsworth

1950   LANDY II

Don's first experience of building ships for Railway Companies was the *Landy II*, a tug built by Dunston's at Hessle for the west coast service of the London Midland Region where he had started as an apprentice draughtsman in 1943. The sea trials of the *Landy II* were marred by extreme difficulty in steering at low speeds. The head would fall away from the intended direction by perhaps 10 or 15 degrees before correcting and was the subject of much learned discussion. Finally a large aperture was cut in the solid skeg and good steering was restored.

Don has a teak straightedge cut from a spare piece of deck planking laid on the ship.

D.I. Harmsworth

1955   LAGA II

When Don joined the Irish Shipping Services in March 1954 a hopper barge had just been ordered from Ferguson Brothers and he was handed the plan approval and supervision of building as his first project. On trials with a dredger in Glasgow docks a dead body was dumped into the hopper by the dredger and stopped proceedings for some hours.

1956   DUKE OF LANCASTER
DUKE OF ARGYLL
DUKE OF ROTHESAY

The order for the above three ships was also about to be placed. These ships were overnight ferries for the Heysham/Belfast service carrying 1,800 passengers and with cabins for about 450 persons. Quotations had shown Denny Bros. slightly lower than Harland & Wolff but Denny's could not deliver the three ships when required so the order was split, Dennys being lead yard for the first delivery, eventually the *Duke of Rothesay*, and the two from Harland's following on. In the event both Harland ships were delivered first and Denny's lagged some way behind. Denny's were supposed to provide Harland's with copies of all plans but with the exception of the basic lines and hydrostatics the two yards produced their own structural and arrangement plans and built to them.

In the Denny ship in order to minimise the size of the shell frames, there was a stringer (stiffener) through the length of the engine and boiler rooms at Lower deck level, but on the Harland ships the frames were made strong enough to be able to dispense with a stringer. The decks were constructed differently too. Denny had clinker pattern plating, while Harland's joggled the beams to give a more flush surface. Remember that all three ships were of mainly riveted construction.

On the machinery side the ships were driven by Pametrada turbines and both these and the boilers were built in the respective shipyard engine works. The Pametrada turbines were the first in British Transport Commission ships with the new thin wall bearings and on the trials of the first ship, the *Duke of Lancaster*, vibration was felt as the ship moved at half speed down Belfast Lough. We returned to the shipyard, investigated and found a bent rotor. The shrouding had slightly rubbed, overheated, bearings had run and, hey presto, we had a problem. It took 5 or 6 weeks before we went back on to trials, this time with no problems but minor problems occurred on each of the other ship trials with the bearings.

On the second and successful trials of the *Duke of Lancaster*, the BBC had a large team of technicians who filmed all aspects of a ship on trials over a full two days, working round the clock but the films were never made into what should have been an interesting documentary.

The 'Dukes' were the first ships fitted with the Mather and Platt mulsi-spray system of fire protection in the machinery spaces continuing the practice of the railway ships to be ahead of the game in safety.

Another innovation for railway ships was the fitting of Viking aluminium lifeboats built by the Wilkes Brothers in their workshops in Ashford, Middlesex. A remarkable feature of those lifeboats was the guarantee for 24 years.

The *Duke of Lancaster* is still in existence as

Duke of Lancaster (*Jim Ashby collection*)

an entertainment centre grounded in an inlet on the North Wales Coast, and after a period in the Greek islands, the 'Argyll' was sold to Hong Kong before a fire in 1995 finished her career.

1956

On the last day of 1956 Don joined the Shipping and International Services Department of the British Transport Commission at Marylebone.

Under the B.T.C. there was a variety of shipping interests, owned or partly owned by the private railway companies prior to nationalisation and managed by their own boards as separate companies. These were the Associated Humber Lines running from Hull and Goole to Amsterdam, Rotterdam, Copenhagen,

Hamburg etc. carrying general cargo and some passengers. The Caledonian Steam Packet Co. based at Gourock and running the Clyde and estuarial services and the Atlantic Steam Navigation Co. founded by Col. Frank Bustard and running Ro-Ro services from Tilbury to Antwerp and from Preston to Larne, initially with ex. tank landing craft bought from the M.O.D after the cessation of hostilities. Their offices were in Whitehall Court.

The British Transport Commission had a Marine Committee with Mr. Leslie Harrington as Chief Officer and Mr. Ted Dewdney as the Marine Officer.

The loss of the *Princess Victoria* spurred the B.T.C. into setting up a separate headquarters department under the management of Leslie

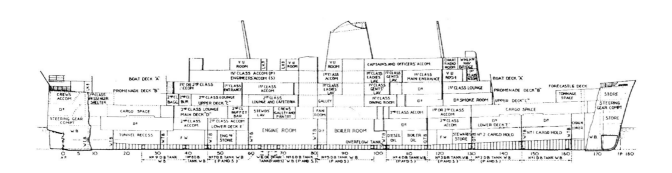

Duke of Rothesay (Ferry Publications Library)

Harrington to design and supervise the building of all new ships for the railway shipping services and for the subsidiary shipping companies. Don joined this newly set-up department on 31st December 1956.

Ted Dewdney was the chief technical officer, Philip Salisbury the naval architect and Don was appointed Chief Draughtsman (of one) although he later had an assistant, Alan Van Der Gert, a marine engineer draughtsman who had served as a sea-going second engineer officer with British India Line after his apprenticeship in the marine workshops in Colombo, Ceylon.

Our first bar chart of ships either in the design stage, on order or building comprised a total of 24 ships. In those hectic days Don did new ship general arrangements, specifications and plan approval for ships under construction, while Philip Salisbury did most of the shipyard visits. He was assisted by Bert Cockett, a shipwright from Belfast, recently foreman shipwright in the Holyhead workshops and then outside superintendent for the new department and who spent most of each week in, and travelling between shipyards from the Clyde to the Isle of Wight.

Above: **Duke of Argyll**.
Top Left: *First Class Dining Room* - **Duke of Lancaster**.
Middle Left: *First Class Lounge* - **Duke of Lancaster**.
Bottom Left: **Duke of Lancaster** *as a car ferry*.
(Photos: Jim Ashby collection & Ferry Publications Library)

Holyhead Ferry I
(Ferry Publications Library)

Colchester
(Ferry Publications Library)

Ferry Publications Library

1957   GLEN SANNOX

Plan approval was carried out on behalf of the Caledonian Steam Packet Co. This was the first U.K. ship to be fitted with inflatable liferafts in fibre glass containers and Don designed the stowage ramps with individual release of the rafts. Access to the rafts was originally by scrambling rope ladders until davit-launched rafts were later introduced.

1957   BARDIC FERRY
1958   IONIC FERRY

These two ships had been ordered by the Atlantic Steam Navigation Co. before the new department was set up and we carried out plan approval and building supervision.

These were the first UK designed and built mainly freight Ro-Ro ships, the term roll-on/ roll-off being coined by the Bustard family after rejecting the term drive-on/ drive off. They did not like the connotation of Do-Do (Dodo) with Bustard – two extinct birds.

At the time these ships were built they were hailed as revolutionary, carrying cargo plus some passengers. The Railways were in the business of moving passengers as a first priority, and although it was quite acceptable to include space for cars it was a departure from their principles to encourage freight to be carried by road. It seemed that the departure of the Atlantic Steam Navigation Co. from the railways conglomerate at the breakup of B.T.C. was welcomed by many in the traditional traffic departments.

1957   ESSEX FERRY

We were again involved in plan approval and some supervision in the later stages of construction and fitting out of the Harwich/ Zeebrugge train ferry in John Brown's Shipyard at Clydebank. This ship was a close repeat of the *Norfolk Ferry* which was built in the same yard in 1951.

1957   LOCHALSH

We were also involved with plan approval and final supervision on this interesting little ship for the Kyle of Lochalsh to Kyleakin (Skye) service. The road vehicles were carried on a bridge-type structure that was secured in a fore and aft line for transit, but rotated through 90 degrees in port and had drop down prow doors to span the gap between ship and shore to allow the loading and discharge of vehicles.

Bardic Ferry (Ferry Publications Library)

Container Venturer *(Jim Ashby collection)*

1957 CONTAINER ENTERPRISE
        CONTAINER VENTURER

These were the first ships owned by the B.T.C. specifically designed for carrying containers. The containers were of course at that day mainly the railway BD type and were moved with a single point lift from a sling picking up four shackles on the container roof.

In the early design stages, Don was aware of the time wasted in loading and unloading. A single line of hatches was intended with the outboard end of every container under the overhang of the hatch side requiring every second container to be drifted fore and aft in addition to the necessary movement outboard from the lowering position.

He drew out proposals with a wider ship, two lines of hatches with the centre coaming supported on a centre line partial bulkhead and with narrower side decks for fore and aft access port and starboard thereby allowing every

container to be lowered freely into position.

Unfortunately the managers would not support a greater beam of ship and thus in 1956 we lost what was virtually a cellular container ship design.

1958 BOLTON ABBEY
1959 MELROSE ABBEY

These two ships were built for Associated Humber Lines for the Hull/ Rotterdam service carrying cargo and 88 passengers.

They were designed and built as general cargo carriers and the Company did not anticipate the onset of ISO containers. Their trade was dying and the later lengthening of the cargo spaces only delayed the closure of the service.

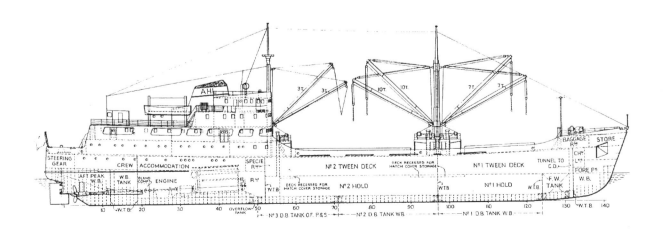

Falaise at Weymouth *(Ferry Publications Library)*

Container Enterprise at Fishguard (Ferry Publications Library)

Bernard McCall

1958 DARLINGTON and WAKEFIELD
1959 HARROGATE, SELBY, YORK
and LEEDS

These were a series of six purely cargo carriers built at Lamont's and Inglis shipyards for the Goole and Continental services of Associated Humber Lines, the *York* being mainly refrigerated for the dairy products trade.

They were designed early in 1957 to a poor commercial remit, as the demise of homogeneous cargo on these routes was clearly in evidence to other shipping companies and they were never successful. As with the *Bolton Abbey* and *Melrose Abbey*, it was not anticipated that their trade was losing out to containerised traffic. None of the eight ships were suitable for container traffic and the Company eventually perished. As a new department, still overcoming the resentment of design being taken from the Regions and subsidiary companies, we often had to try to make the best of poor commercial remits.

Jim Ashby collection

1958 ISLE OF ELY and COLCHESTER

Two ships built to operate on the Parkeston Quay to Rotterdam service for the Eastern Region. Again they were ships built to an outdated commercial remit on a similar basis to the AHL vessels, and it was a struggle from the outset to maintain profitability.

Maid of Kent (Ferry Publications Library)

This was the first fully enclosed vehicle carrier built for the Channel service between Dover and Boulogne but the configuration made for slow loading and discharge. The after end of the vehicle space had a clear height of 11'2", sufficient for the coaches of the day and these were individually manoeuvred via an electrically operated turntable aft to enable the space to be filled. The forward part of the space was in two levels and sufficient clear height for cars only.

Bow loading and discharging had not been contemplated for the ferry traffic other than the double ended estuarial craft on the Isle of Wight services.

We carried out plan approval and supervision and it seemed odd that in a 'modern' ship the officers had to traverse the open deck to go from their accommodation to the bridge. She was subsequently fitted with a 'flying bridge', and access to this was completely open.

The *Maid of Kent* was the first ship that had the public spaces designed by an interior design architect. They were appointed by the B.T.C. Design Panel to provide the decorative schemes and select the materials for the public rooms. Ward and Austin (later Ward Associates) carried out the design work and this was the start of an association with B.R. ships that remained unbroken for 25 years: a proud record.

The choice of design had previously been left to the Marine Managers of the Company or Region. The practice had been to ask ship furnishers to quote for the project giving details of materials and generally colour perspectives for the large spaces and orders were placed on that basis with all details of basic construction of panelling built in furniture, ceilings etc. being left to the shipyard and the main outfitters. Ward and Austin began the practice of providing selections of materials, plan and elevation views, colour perspectives of all major spaces and a specification for the outfitting firms to quote against. Quotes were also allowed from the shipyards who had joiner work departments large enough to cope with such a project ie. Swan Hunters and Harland & Wolff would quote.

Above: **Maid of Kent -** Main car deck *(Jim Ashby collection)*
Below: **Maid of Kent** - Tea Lounge *(Jim Ashby collection)*

The *Maid of Kent* was also the first B.R. ship with a bow thrust unit which was in this case a Voith Schneider propeller of about 4 tonnes side thrust.

Alone amongst the car carriers, the *Maid of Kent* had a shipyard-designed jigger winch, hydraulically operated to raise and lower the stern door.

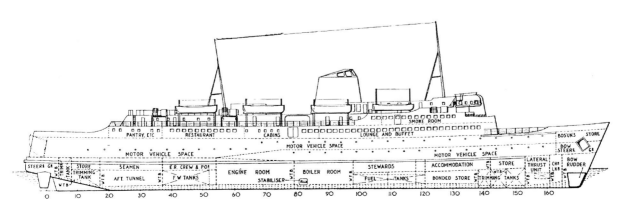

Harwich-Zeebrugge train ferry *(Ferry Publications Library)*

Dave Hocquard

1959 ELK and MOOSE

These were two cargo ships built for the Southern Region services from Southampton to the Channel Islands. Once more they were designed to an out dated commercial remit and were not able to compete with the later vehicular traffic.

Miles Cowsill

1959 MEECHING

The *Meeching* was built in P.K. Harris in Appledore to Burness Kendal Hydroconic tug design before the yard became Appledore Shipbuilders.

Old Mr Harris was still firmly in charge and there was a real family atmosphere in the yard. The trials were a bit of a disaster. We needed to

be over the Bideford Bar at high tide and could not return again before the next tide. Unfortunately when we got out, the fog came down and we had 10 hours of stooging about on a course between somewhere off Westward Ho! and Lundy Island, much to the disgust of a colleague who slumped on the outer casings slowly turning shades of green as we corkscrewed in swell hour after hour. We cleared the bar inward late in the evening and found clear weather in the river.

1959 FRESHWATER

This ship was a radical departure from the preceding ship built for Isle of Wight services, the *Farringford* which was a double ended diesel-electric paddle ferry.

The *Freshwater* returned to the pre-war *Lymington* style of 2 Voith Schneider cycloidal propellers, port side forward and starboard side aft.

Highly manoeuvrable, she was a very successful ship on the Lymington/ Yarmouth service carrying 620 passengers and 26 cars.

She was the last I.O.W. ship we fitted with deck sockets for sheep pens, not that Don can remember any being carried.

The ship also had painted areas of the main deck to be kept clear of cars to allow sufficient deck space per passenger if and when a full complement of 620 passengers was carried.

At the end of her Sealink career she was sold to Western Ferries (Clyde) Ltd. and was renamed *Sound of Seil*.

1960 KYLEAKIN

This ship was a repeat of the *Lochalsh* which made plan approval easy.

Freshwater (John Hendy)

Slieve Donard (Jim Ashby collection)

1960   SLIEVE DONARD

Don had done the early design work before leaving Euston and this was followed closely in the final ship. She was a cattle carrier primarily with provision for horses, sheep and surprisingly cars.

All her predecessors were steam ships and this was quite a departure.

It was also departure to carry trade cars. Flush hatches were fitted, one with a tonnage opening, a shore access vehicle door was fitted at the stern and a maximum of 150 cars could be accommodated in the tween deck and the open deck aft. Cattle and horse pens were arranged with flush mounts and a new type of decking was laid in the animal spaces. Don had been disturbed some years before at seeing the state of the steel decks in the cattle areas on the *Great Western*, the Fishguard to Waterford passenger, cargo and cattle ship when she was on refit. The 2.5 inch thick concrete, the normal deck for cattle spaces, had cracked in many places as the ship had flexed. Cattle urine had then seeped through the cracks, spread between the concrete and the steel deck and major part of the structure, both plating and beams corroded through and had to be replaced. It was surprising that the loss of a substantial portion of the structure had not lead to distortion but none was apparent.

Don looked at various deck coverings and eventually proposed a stiffened asphalt produced by Durastic which would flex with the ship, was fully resistant to urine and petrol spills and had excellent adherence to the steel. It proved a good choice and was very successful.

Tenders were received from a number of yards of which Ailsa at Troon was the lowest with Denny's some way down the list. However Denny's tender provoked considerable interest as, in true style, they guaranteed to obtain the required speed with less powerful engines.

The specified main engines were British Polar M48M diesels. Denny's proposed fitting two x 6 cylinder engines whereas Ailsa stated that they required two x 7 cylinder units to provide the necessary speed. The decision was made to build at Ailsa but as the Supt. Marine Engineer did not like the imbalance of 7 cylinder engines, two 8 cylinder units were fitted. The guaranteed speed was, if memory serves Don correctly, achieved on about 60% of the maximum continuous rating of the engines.

British Polar requested permission to use one of the two engines on their stand at the marine exhibition and, as delivery was not in question,

Slieve Donard - Cattle pens *(Jim Ashby collection)*

permission was readily given. The apprentices were set to work on the engine to give a very high quality finish for the exhibition, hand painted, chromed, polished etc. and, of course, the second engine had to match and the result was a particularly smart engine room when they were installed in the ship.

The *Slieve Donard* was often used as a summer relief at both Holyhead and Stranraer to carry additional cars while the drivers and passengers travelled on the regular passenger ferry.

On one of the old 'Slieve' cattle carriers the engineer officer on watch was surprised to meet a cow face to face in the main machinery room on a night trip he will long remember. The beast had escaped from the stall, wandered along the deck, poked her head through the open door to the machinery space and we assumed the ship's motion had thrown her down the stairs on to the platforms where she was having a look around when discovered.

D.I. Harmsworth

1960   RED NAB

A close repeat of the *Laga II* (1955) but there was a real saga behind the financial case for the ship. The new hopper barge was to be built to replace an existing hopper built in 1902. By their cunning methods of working up the original cost on an annual basis from 1902 to date, using inflation etc. in their calculations, the Railway accountants had arrived at what they knew the ship should cost. Fortunately we knew the cost of the sister ship which was considerably higher than that produced by the accountants. We then had to carry out a long exercise showing how much the new ship would differ from the 1902 ship so that the accountants could produce a cost of "betterment" and prove they were right all the time. That silly exercise took over a year.

1961   CAESAREA and SARNIA

These were classic passenger ferries built to run on the Southern Region services between Weymouth and the Channel Isles and were the only cross-Channel ferries we owned that were built by J. Samuel White at Cowes, Isle of Wight.

They were the first ships actually ordered by the new Shipping & International Services Department for a railway region and the design and general arrangement were produced largely by the new department to a close commercial remit by the Southern Region commercial and technical departments. All survey work, plan approval and technical discussions with the yard were carried out by the new department, but the traditional railway practice of appointing a standby Chief Engineer Officer as soon as the keel was laid was still followed but from that time on he concentrated on machinery and pipework and construction and fitting out was supervised by ourselves from H.Q.

These ships were also a departure for the Southern Region. Having lost ships in the War and having their normal replacement programme disrupted by hostilities, the old Southern Railway had reserved a series of berths in Denny's Dumbarton yard.

The new Channel Islands ships were to be built on a cost plus basis of a fixed cost for hull and machinery and for all subcontracted items the Owners were given a number of quotations

Sarnia (Kevin Le Scelleur)

together with the cost allowed by the yard for each item. It was then the choice of the Owners to select the quotation which reflected the quality they required and to pay the difference to the yard. It was very nice for the yard to have all the risk taken out of estimating but the Owners felt satisfied they were maintaining a standard of quality. It was the practice of the new department to specify the quality and require the yard to supply and build accordingly.

During the building of these ships, Philip Salisbury left the department and was replaced by Tony Rogan who came from Lloyd's.

The two ships had White/ Gilljet bow thrust units. The *Caesarea* and *Sarnia* were the first ships on which we fitted rotary steering gears, as we had not sufficient space in the bow for the normal ram gear for the bow rudder.

The ships were the first to be panelled out in melamine surfaced Marinite asbestos board and generated a whole new series of joiner work details.

When the *Caesarea* and *Sarnia* were ordered it was decided by the Design Panel that the B.T.C. Chief Architect, Dr. Curtis, should prepare the decorative designs for the first ship and Ward and Austin the second ship. We passed to Dr. Curtis's department a general arrangement for the ship and were astonished to have this returned to us with major modifications. Without any consultation the main engine room, boiler room and other below main deck spaces had been moved and public spaces were totally reorganised, passenger and crew cabin areas had been transposed in some areas, moved to other decks and given totally different sizes. When it was pointed out that such modifications were not within their remit we were informed that they were the architects and they would decide the interior arrangement of the ship. We then asked on what basis they had decided the possible and permissible length of watertight compartments below the bulkhead deck and this was met with blank stares. Things got a bit hot for a time but eventually we proceeded with our general arrangement with minor modifications to suit the decorative layout.

Following that experience all subsequent ships went to Ward and Austin.

We carried on in this way for almost 25 years until Sealink was bought by Sea Containers and it was decided that new looks, new ideas and new people were to be used on new projects.

An interesting incident occurred at the launch of the *Sarnia*. Bert Cockett, not having been invited to attend by the Southern Region who had prepared the Owner's guest list, was invited personally by Sir James Milne, Chairman of the Samuel White shipyard. Having been instructed that he should not attend, Bert advised that he was taking a day's holiday and what he did on that day was his business! Bert and his wife, Edna, crossed to the Isle of Wight on the same ferry as the official Owner's party who, on arrival at Ryde were directed into buses to take them to the Cowes yard. Eyebrows were raised when Sir James Milne's Rolls Royce arrived alongside the buses to chauffeur Bert and Edna to the ceremony ! An example of the esteem with which Bert was held by everyone he worked with.

Vibration in high powered, light structured, ferries was always a problem, the origin normally being in the region of the propellers. The *Caesarea* was no exception and high frequency vibration in the restaurant area could not be cured by the usual expedient of adding a few structural pillars.

Tony made a crossing to investigate during which Capt. Newton demonstrated his party trick at the Captain's Table. This was a readily reproducible phenomenon in which a cup of coffee placed in the centre of the table firstly acquired concentric rings due the vibration. The surface then quartered itself into four humps which grew until they collapsed, simultaneously, into the centre of the cup whereupon one globule of coffee was propelled vertically to a height of about four inches above the surface. The globule then dropped back into the cup and the whole process repeated itself !

The vibration problem was found, with the help of the British Ship Research Association, to originate from the bossing supports on the propeller shafts. This was not a new problem since it had been present in the 'Duke' class and the solution was the same as for the 'Dukes': fitting struts to prevent 'waggling' of the bossings. This same problem was to haunt us in future designs until it was eliminated in the *Antrim Princess* by adopting an open shaft tube arrangement supported by 'A' brackets at the propeller.

Ferry Publications Library

1961 CERDIC FERRY
1962 DORIC FERRY

These two ships were close repeats of the *Bardic Ferry* (1957) but were 23 ft. longer with more powerful main engines and 2 knots faster in speed. Accommodation and vehicle spaces were generally as the earlier ships.

A notable feature of the A.S.N. Co. operation was the use of modern towing units to load and

Camber Queen (Jim Ashby collection)

discharge trailers which made up a high proportion of vehicles carried. The towing units had swing and movable cabs, could be driven at speed either forward or in reverse and enabled rapid loading and discharging in the ports. With the high proportion of trailers, through loading was not a great advantage and was not seriously considered.

1961   FISHBOURNE and CAMBER QUEEN

These two ships were similar to the *Freshwater* (1959) being built to the same lines and construction plans up to main deck level. Indeed when the technical manager of Philips of Dartmouth came to the first meeting after the order was placed, he took back with him a brief case bulging with a copy of every "as fitted" plan produced for the *Freshwater*. His smile went almost full circle as he found all his design work handed over on a plate.

The passenger complement was much lower on these two ferries as the Portsmouth route was much less a classic foot-passenger route than Lymington to Yarmouth.

These two ships had the first hydraulically operated bow and stern vehicle ramp doors, these previously being operated by electric winch and chains.

Much discussion took place concerning the machinery and stair casings. We put forward designs with a central casing with the deck over supported at the sides by an extended shell but the Southern Region insisted that side casings had to be fitted to allow a clear run through the centre of the main deck to allow for "Queen Mary's" the 66 ft. long aeroplane component carriers, ferrying fuselages and wings etc. from the Island.

However, even though the ships were built with side casings, they never carried the long loaders and for the life of the ships, drivers had to reverse vehicles on every trip.

While these two ships were fitting-out, the Department of Trade redefined the dimensions of ships under the navigation signals regulations and we found we were a few feet too long to be able to continue with a single mast at midships with navigation lights on both sides. We found it necessary to fit an additional mast at each end on a gantry arrangement to be able to obtain the necessary separation. They looked most odd.

All our new ship construction was governed by The Board's Conditions of Contract (BTC 6) which were pretty tough on the Shipbuilder. It was important to know the detail of these conditions when in discussion with builders. Tony was caught with his pants down when Mr. Street, the yard's Technical Director, warned that completion of the two ferries would be delayed by late delivery of diesel alternators. When Tony protested that this was the yard's problem and that they should seriously contemplate the financial consequences of late delivery, he was quietly advised that BTC 6 required all deliveries to be made, where practicable, by rail. The diesel alternators were on a wagon, lost on the then neolithic freight system ! A quick telephone call to Don in London set enquiries in motion which located the wagon within 24 hours and saved the day.

1961   CATHERINE, EDITH and ROSE

When the Dartford Tunnel opened, the traditional Gravesend vehicle ferry service closed and in readiness for this, we built three new passenger-only ferries to continue the service over to Tilbury, mainly as a commuting service for dock workers. The three ships replaced the original passenger carriers *Catherine* (1903), *Edith* (1912), and *Rose* (1901) built by A.W. Robertson, London and all of which were fitted with coal burning, steam reciprocating, engines.

Edith *(Jim Ashby collection)*

The old vehicle ferries were *Mimie* (1927) built by Ferguson Bros. and *Tessa* (1924) which was built by Lytham Shipbuilding Co.

The new ships were 110 ft. overall and propelled by a single Voith Schneider unit on the centre aft. The Department of Transport insisted that because they were passenger ships operating on a busy waterway, the ships should have a rudder in case the V.S. unit failed. How we were going to steer without forward motion did not appear to worry the Department.

One, or rather six, notable features of the ferries were the gangways. These were hydraulically operated, jack-knife in action and had to be rapidly operated to accommodate impatient dockers. They were designed by Vickers Hydraulic Division and were capable of being deployed within seconds of the ship tying up, the sections being upright when stowed with self-stowing safety side rails.

When the level of Thames traffic fell dramatically, the third ship *Rose* was dispatched under her own power to the Clyde where she became the Largs – Cumbrae ferry, *Keppel*.

1961 CALEDONIAN PRINCESS

This ship was the eventual replacement for the ill fated *Princess Victoria* and was a stern loading passenger and vehicle carrier built by Denny's. She was the last cross Channel ferry to be built at the famous Dumbarton shipyard

which went into liquidation in September 1963.

Vehicle carrying services between Stranraer and Larne had been run on a summer only basis with one of the Dover train ferries, usually the *Hampton Ferry*, which had been on that route during World War II, but this was the new start the route needed and was welcomed by all at the town and port of Stranraer.

Paint on ships bottoms has been the subject of many discussions and on the *Caledonian Princess* and later ships in Stranraer we had some discussion on whether it was essential to paint the flat of bottom. Each year in dry-dock the lowest areas were polished clean of paint by the scouring of sand as the ships passed over the shallows in Loch Ryan.

This was the first ship fitted with the new

Above: First Class bar · **Caledonian Princess**
Below: Second Class Cafeteria · **Caledonian Princess**

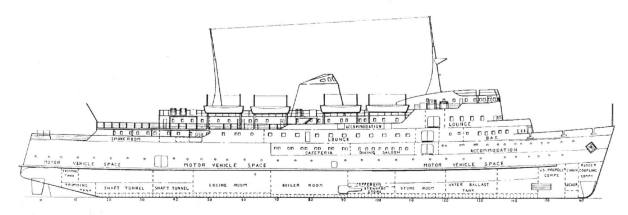

Denny /Brown/ A.E.G. folding stabilisers. We had an agreement with Denny's that if this new type was not as effective as the normal type they would be replaced and in fact space was left in the boiler room to enable the normal type to be installed. Denny's were correct in their forecast and we continued to fit the new type.

A further 'modern' feature of the ship was the Voith Schneider lateral thrust unit at the bow of about 4 tonnes thrust.

As this was the Department's first real vehicle carrier, we decided to investigate the ventilation of the car decks with the ventilation contractor Thermotank, now APV Hall International. We calculated the emission of exhaust gases, volume of space, density of toxicity of the resulting foul air and came to the conclusion that to provide a decent and safe working space for the crew members marshalling the cars, we needed to fit an outfit of fans that would give us 600 cu.ft per minute per car of exhaust ventilation with natural supply by the shore ramp access door and some mechanical supply by fans.

This became our standard in Sealink for many years and was considerably higher than the subsequent International Maritime Organisation (I.M.O.) norm.

We had a number of fans and these exhausted the air via a network of ducts leading from all part of the vehicle decks which gave us many problems in obtaining adequate clear heights.

As part of the decoration of the public rooms, Ward & Austin commissioned David Gentleman to design a pair of murals for the 2nd class cafeteria to wrap around the uptake casings. The murals evoked the continuous pastoral and sea-girt story of Celtic life and were reproduced in black and white by Warerite. Each was about 25 feet long and had a terrific impact.

Similar turbine problems to those encountered some years earlier on the 'Duke' steamers dogged the completion, and once more we had to limp back from trials, make repairs, and try again.

The ship finished service in 1981 and is today a Glasgow night-club on the Clyde.

1963   AVALON

The last classic passenger ship we designed and possibly the finest looking ship we ever built, the *Avalon* was a replacement for the pre-war *Duke of York* (1935) built in Belfast for the Heysham service and transferred to Parkeston Quay post nationalisation. The *Duke of York* had two close shaves, once, in collision with an American warship and, again, when a mine blew off the forward end but both times she was repaired and re-entered service.

The *Avalon* was a passenger and mail ship with some cargo space used mainly for perishables and a few craned-on cars. She carried 750 passengers with 618 in cabin berths. She was the last of an era. British Rail ran the night service ferries to the Hook of Holland with three ships, one outward bound, one inward bound each night, both standing at the quay side each day, the third ship being on standby ready to take service at a few hours notice except during survey periods. The Dutch ran the day service on a similar three ship basis.

The ship was designed with fine lines at each end to achieve a service speed of 21.5 knots and so we could not easily fit the normal 4 ram steering gears and the AEG rotary vane units were fitted.

At the stern a separate unit was fitted to each rudder with electronic linking and on at least two occasions this failed to act, one occasion resulting in the stern ramming the quay at the Hook and punching a hole in the shell above the waterline.

When we designed the *Avalon*, we had a nice curve across the bridge front that extended right to the ends of the open bridge wings. We also

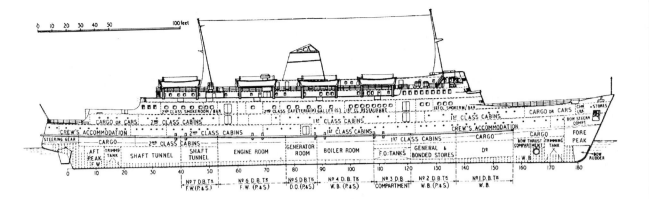

fitted a flying bridge over, but this had bulwarks on the forward and aft sides at right angles to the ship's centreline.

We were reviled by the navigating officers on the ship as the wind and weather hit the bulwark of the flying bridge and was deflected straight down on the crew standing below on the normal bridge wing. As an easy solution, we suggested fitting a deflector plate but this was not done.

For some years ships had been panelled in melamine surfaced Marinite asbestos board with structural fire protection insulation, generally of sprayed limpet asbestos in the accommodation and service spaces. On the *Avalon*, because of the dusty, unpleasant atmosphere when working with Marinite and sprayed asbestos, we changed to fire resisting chipboard produced by Weyroc for the panelling and insulated A Class divisions with fibre glass slabs and blankets in accommodation and service spaces.

However because of several doubts as to the efficiency of fibre glass, we did not use it again for A Class insulation.

The fire resisting chipboard was welcomed by the joiners and outfitters particularly as it was easier to work and had better screw holding properties than Marinite. Our usual test for screw holding for a proposed new board was to fit a coat hook and see how difficult or easy it was to wrench off.

The **Avalon** seen prior to her launch in March 1963

Jim Ashby collection

The *Avalon* was a popular cruise ship for some years with regular passengers returning year after year cruising to destinations from North Africa to the North Cape.

This was the first passenger ship to be fitted with biological sewage treatment plant which was the Biogest system supplied under licence by G.D. Peters in Slough.

Again at the time of building, the shortsightedness of the British Rail traffic departments was evident. It was felt that as passenger accompanied car traffic would not

Avalon *(Ferry Publications Library)*

Duke of Rothesay *(Ferry Publications Library)*

develop on the Harwich/ Hook route, this would remain a purely 'classic' service.

The *Avalon's* launch was postponed by a Clyde tug-men's strike. As a consequence the official naming ceremony was performed after delivery by Lady Beeching alongside at Parkeston Quay. The shipbuilders devised a swinging cradle to hold the diamond scratched champagne bottle. Bert Cockett's eagle eye noted that bunting added to the forward area was likely to cushion the bottle as it descended. He was, as always, right and the champagne bottle failed to explode on impact. But no-one spotted Bert's hand, with hammer, appearing from a side-scuttle (porthole) to smash the bottle a fraction of a second later !

Jim Ashby collection

1963   CAMBRIDGE FERRY

A train ferry built by Hawthorn Leslie provided our first visit to that yard. We were given the task of designing a new train ferry to carry more freight than the three existing Harwich/ Zeebrugge ships but still under the constraints of the same berth and port limits.

We managed to carry 300 tons of additional deadweight on 9" less draft with same length between perpendiculars and the same moulded beam.

This was the first rail ferry where we fitted recessed rails for the wagons apart from at the stern as at that time shallow points rails were not available. We found enthusiastic help from our permanent way colleagues in British Rail who volunteered to a man to assist in track layout and also to help with setting out on the ship. They were, however, hidebound by their B.R. design standards which assumed 'main line' working situations. Having negotiated with them more appropriate track separation distances and sharper curvatures than normal (speeds of rakes of wagons being in the order of 5 mph), they produced a superb track layout plan which easily met our needs, but we were puzzled by the steel equivalents of sleepers they had included. It seemed that they were unable to comprehend rails not being supported by the conventional sleeper ! The rails were set in recessed channels with the excess space filled with asphalt.

We also designed and fitted a sophisticated

system of overhead rails and gantries to pick up railway type containers from the open deck aft and transfer them along the train deck to the stowed positions. This system was removed a few years later with the introduction of I.S.O. containers as the additional height and weight could not be accommodated.

We later fitted a hinged ramp to enable trade cars to be driven to the extended upper deck level.

The *Cambridge Ferry* was distinctive in profile as she had both masts forward of the funnel. She was the first ship in the fleet to be fitted with controllable pitch propellers and also the first to be fitted with a 'Flume' water tank stabiliser, designed not for crew comfort but to minimise the risk of de-railment in adverse weather.

She was the first ferry since the *Shepperton Ferry* in 1935 to be built on the Tyne and this was the start of a new and happy relationship with the river's builders and ship repairers over the next few years.

The rail link span at Harwich had had a chequered career. Originally built for service at Richborough on the Kent coast to enable trains to be loaded on to ships to run to Calais in World War I, the terminal was finally abandoned in 1919.

The Great Eastern Railway Co. bought the terminal fittings, took the linkspan on a barge in tow for Harwich, saw it sink on the way, had it salvaged some time later and opened the new rail ship service from Harwich Town to Zeebrugge in 1924.

The *Cambridge Ferry* was laid up for some time and during one of her periods of idleness was used to transport military vehicles, tanks etc. to and from the Continent for a Dickie Attenborough film, she being the only ship available that could take the concentrated deck loads of some of the vehicles and tanks.

Ferry Publications Library

1964   GAELIC FERRY

We carried out some design work on this ship for A.S.N. Co. including design general arrangement and specification but it was largely based on the previous *Cerdic Ferry* (1961). On this ship the Owners wished to use the tank top for additional vehicle space. We proposed a hinged ramp recessed into the tank top, raised to the main deck for loading and discharging and lowered with a full load of vehicles. However the Owners opted for a cheaper alternative of a fixed ramp with the necessary hinged cover in the main deck, thus losing the area of the ramp in vehicle stowage for the life of the ship.

plan view to that of the *Lord Warden*, the standard for Channel service, to ensure compatibility with port terminals and we continued the practice of fitting linkspans attached to the shore bridges that landed on the stern of the ship with the ship's door hinging upwards. Turntables were fitted to assist in loading vehicles as the ship was only stern loading. The stern door was operated by a Kone hydraulic hinge, the only example on a Sealink ship.

While alongside at Holyhead, a large section of the quay collapsed and damaged the forward shell on the port side which resulted in the ship being taken out of service. We had suggested to the civil engineers that with the bow thrust unit constantly washing against the same part of a 100 year old quay, they may require to fit some strengthening but nothing was done until it collapsed.

1965 HOLYHEAD FERRY I

You may say what a name for a ship. John Bustard had moved from Atlantic Steam Nav. Co. to be the Manager of the Irish Shipping Services at Euston and as all the ASN ships names ended in 'Ferry' so we had the *Holyhead Ferry 1*. The '1' was added as John Bustard expected to have more than one.

At a later ship launch in Eire, the Chief Customs Officer in Holyhead asked Don what idiot had dreamt up the name just as John Bustard joined the group. Don managed to pass it off and John wandered away again without speaking.

This was one of the last two steam ships. The stern of the ship had to be of similar contour in

1965 DOVER

When tenders were received for the *Holyhead Ferry I*, it had become apparent that an extra 'slot' was to be made available at Dover Eastern Docks for the summer of 1965 and to retain the B.R. percentage of ship workings it was decided to order a second vessel. Urgent talks took place with Hawthorn Leslie to see if a second ship could be delivered in time for the 1965 season but these were not successful and the second lowest tenderers, Swan Hunter, were awarded the contract for the second ship based on their original tender for the *Holyhead Ferry I*. Negotiations were immediately entered into for some fairly large modifications to suit the Dover route, e.g. a duty-free shop, galley moved aft,

Teabar - **Holyhead Ferry I** *(Jim Ashby collection)*

Main car deck - **Dover** *(Jim Ashby collection)*

Hengist and *Horsa* under construction *(Ferry Publications Library)*

St George (Ferry Publications Library)

public rooms extended and modified with a larger capacity for cars at mezzanine deck level.

We still fitted hatches forward on both ships partly for loading mail by crane and partly for removal of vehicles if the stern door was put out of action.

Hatches fitted over the aft end of the vehicle space were MacGregor flush watertight pattern and incorporated tonnage openings at the forward end of the hatch. These were anomalies to enable the vehicle deck to be deleted from the tonnage. The main hatch, 20 ft. x 12 ft., had a removable beam at the forward end which formed the after end of a raised coaming of a hatch 12 ft. wide x 6 ft. fore and aft which had loose wooden boards and canvas covers retained by wood wedges to obtain watertightness. This was the tonnage hatch and was not allowed by the Tonnage Regulations to be flush. It was only opened for annual survey. The *Dover* was the last ship from a U.K. yard for some years that was delivered early and for that the shipyard got a bonus.

Twenty or thirty workmen travelled with the ship to Dover after trials to finish off the public rooms while familiarisation of crew and port trials were carried out.

The architect Misha Black was once asked to comment on a set of designs for the ship prepared by Ward & Austin and demanded that in one area there should be a glass wall. This unfortunately happened to be on 'A' class fire bulkhead.

Some may remember that there was a competition run by B.R. in conjunction with the regional newspapers for a name for the new ship. Few will not be amused that the name chosen by "popular demand" was as inspiring as *Dover*.

After that John Bustard was asked to research a generic series of names that had not been used before, had connections with all areas of the U.K. and was fairly extensive. To our surprise he had the imagination to suggest the names of ancient Kings and others associated with the Dark Ages, hence *Hengist*, *Rhodri Mawr*, *Caedmon*, *Cenwulf* etc, names that we are all familiar with.

1967 PORTREE and BROADFORD

We had a small interest in these two ships and carried out plan approval work after consultation on early design.

1967 ANTRIM PRINCESS

This was the first B.R. cross Channel passenger ship for many years to have diesel main engines. The *Hibernia* and *Cambria* in 1949 were the previous such vessels. The chief technical officer of the Shipping and International Services Department, Ted Dewdney, was a 'died-in-the-wool' steam engineer, and insisted on steam machinery as long as he was able to resist the demands of Tony Rogan and David Barwell to bring the ships up to modern standards. It was also the accepted principle that steam machinery was quieter and had little or no vibration. The noise and vibration of auxiliary diesels was ignored.

The onset of modern diesel machinery brought about a necessary change in funnel design, and after much internal discussion, calculations and sketches by Tony Rogan, a new shape was evolved and proved in wind tunnel tests which were carried out at Swan Hunter's for the *St. George* but used to devise the geometry also of the *Antrim Princess'* funnel. With variations to ensure smoke clearance with different superstructures and relative positioning from the bridge front, this funnel became a symbol of the fleet.

Antrim Princess *(Jim Ashby collection)*

It was also a big departure in that we had a bow visor and inner bow door, reflecting the increasing role of the lorry traffic needing through loading for maximum utilisation.

At the time the ship was building in Hawthorn Leslie's, the Danish ferry *Winston Churchill* came into Parkeston Quay after a very rough passage from Esbjerg when she had come through Force 12 gales and mountainous seas. Don was asked to get down to Parkeston Quay as quickly as possible to see the damage to the visor.

To his astonishment the visor was only secured to the ship with a double line of wire mooring rope heroically run from the capstan via mooring eyes in the bulwarks, round the stem and back on to the forward deck, caught on a bollard, run round the stem a second time and tightened up on the capstan. The visor was initially supported on two major steel box arms which were hinged in two massive tabernacles. The tabernacles were bolted down to doubled deck plates with 32 x 1.25 inch diameter bolts all of which had sequentially fractured. The visor had been held weathertight at the joint with the shell by eight 1.25 inch diameter bottle screws, manually operated. All these had either fractured or pulled one end free from shell or visor. The visor was in fact hanging on to the ship only by means of the wire rope and at a much reduced speed the ship had reached Parkeston Quay safely. The inner bow door was fully intact.

As the *Antrim Princess* was our first ship with a visor we had urgent talks with Hawthorn Leslie and Cargospeed, the cargo access equipment suppliers, to satisfy ourselves that we had adequate security.

The *Antrim Princess* was our first ship with A.C. electrical power but for some years we fitted Ward Leonard AC/DC machinery to all capstans and windlasses to retain the higher flexibility of control that D.C had over A.C.

We suffered a serious mishap during the fitting-out of the ship. Steve Dickman had just joined the team with his main duties as installation engineer and on his first morning in the shipyard, as he was changing to go down to the ship, an S.O.S. for him was sent out. We were told an engine had fallen over and this in fact had happened.

To suit the cranage, both main Crossley Pielstick engines had been lowered down through an aperture left in the structure on the starboard side. The port engine, first on board, had been fleeted over to the centreline and left standing on wooden blocks on the tank top. The starboard engine had then been lowered on to blocks directly above the starboard engine seating. The structure above was closed up and fitting out of both accommodation and machinery spaces progressed. When the time came to move the port engine to its seating chain blocks, jacks, sliding blocks etc., were all assembled and the

move commenced but when the engine was almost in position, the wooden blocks gave way and the engine slowly toppled outboard. Luckily it went outboard and missed the fitters who were all inboard. The engine weighed about 70 tonnes and would have crushed anything in its path. After discussion it was agreed that the engine should be returned to Crossley's for a thorough check and apertures were cut in the structure above on the port side where public rooms and cabins were well advanced. When the engine was examined it was found that only superficial damage had occurred to components plus a couple of small indents in the sump casing. The damage to personnel was one crushed hand, one badly cut thumb and a whole lot of pride. A very lucky escape.

This ship was the first in which we fitted portable mezzanine decks and they were supplied by Cargospeed.

The shipyard had ordered the outfit of watertight doors from Scandinavia but as delivery of these was a long way behind schedule, the order was cancelled. We 'borrowed' the Stone's water tight doors already delivered to Swan Hunter's for the next ship in our programme, the *St. George*, and Stone's supplied a replacement set in time for the Harwich ship.

The *Antrim Princess* saw the first Mather and Platt drencher system in the vehicle decks. Previously the vehicle spaces on car carriers had a sprinkler system fitted with water spray curtains in vertical line with the major fire divisions in the machinery spaces below and accommodation areas above. This arrangement had necessitated a four feet gap between vehicles at the spray curtains and had lead to a lot of broken stowage when larger vehicles were carried and it became almost impossible to fit adequate water spray curtains in conjunction with raised mezzanine deck panels. We therefore welcomed this advance in fire protection and safety.

With the drenchers being activated manually in large sections, it was essential to be able to quickly disperse the large quantities of water produced. We calculated water emission, flow along a sheered deck, speed of evacuation into scuppers and proposed to the Department that we should fit 6 inch diameter scuppers at intervals of 20 feet at the ship's side and at intervals of 30 feet along the inboard casings. The Department accepted this and it became the standard.

When we were involved with the Department of Transport in the 1960's looking at new I.M.O proposals for safety of ships and passengers, one of the major items was safety on vehicle decks – safety from fire and also safety for the health of working crew on the car decks. We noticed in a non-marine trade magazine a reference to a firm, Becorit, who supplied gas detecting equipment to coal mines. We were at the time concerned about

Essex Ferry (Ferry Publications Library)

the effects of petrol and diesel engine exhaust fumes on the crew and of the danger of concentrations of petrol or oil vapour that may become explosive if in contact with cigarettes or electrical sparks. On enquiry to the firm they were happy to investigate the problem and soon came up with a solution – a gas detection system that could detect both toxic and explosive concentrations of gases with separate heads for each type and we fitted these for some years before they became a statutory requirement.

1968   ST. GEORGE

The *St. George* was one of a pair of ships that were introduced on the Hook of Holland route to initiate a vehicle carrying service. She sailed from her home port of Parkeston Quay at midday, arrived at the Hook at 6.00 p.m., left the Hook at 10.00 p.m., before arriving at Parkeston Quay at 6.00 a.m. The Dutch ship was the *Koningin Juliana*, built in Cammell Laird, which sailed the opposite leg of the two ship service.

These two ships, doing a round trip in every 24 hours, replaced six ships on the old less intensive service.

There had been much discussion between the two companies (B.R. and our Dutch partners, S.M.Z.) to agree the commercial content of the ships as it was essential to have the same cabin berth capacity and the same vehicle stowage capacity. We did most of the development drawing work and although the Dutch Owners made modifications to public room layout and cabin disposition, it was largely our general arrangement that formed the basis for the two ships.

When the orders were placed, the *St. George* at Swan's, the *Koningin Juliana* at Cammell's, long discussions took place over arrangements of shafting, skegs, positions and size of rudders etc. and it was eventually decided that even though the lines below the water line were to be the same, the stern arrangements on the two ships were to be different.

The Dutch ship also had a full metre of additional overall length as the Owners wanted a more pronounced curve on the stem above the waterline. This proved a mistake as a few years later, after having suffered frequent damage to the visor, the ship had a new visor fitted which was one metre shorter than the original. The

'Juliana' also suffered from a serious fire on board while fitting out at Cammell Laird which delayed completion for a few weeks.

The service requirement for the ships was for 21 knots on the daylight run and for 16 or 17 knots on the night service, a perfect arrangement for 4 engines. Ruston A.O. diesels were selected for the *St. George* as the optimum prime movers and these engines of innovative design were bedded in pairs on to a resiliently mounted raft, two engines running into one gearbox also on the raft with flexible couplings to the main shafts.

Much has been written, both good and bad, about these engines but the selection was made on the performance predictions, the well known reliability of the engine makers, and the perfect suitability on all counts for the installation. Sealink and its B.R. predecessors had never lacked courage in fitting the first of a generation and this was a further example of leading the field. Although the engines did not prove the spectacular success predicted for them, it is important to remember that the *St. George* never lost a sailing due to main engine faults. Trips were done on three engines and occasionally the ship arrived on two but a trip was never lost and that cannot be said about many installations.

Noise and vibration problems, evident on trials were tackled with limited success. The positioning of the first class accommodation aft was a departure from the norm and this was the area most affected at speeds of above about 19.5 knots and also during manoeuvring when entering or leaving the berths. Fortunately the night service speed of about 17 knots was free of problems.

We did lose a day and a half on trials with a propeller problem. We were at sea on the Saturday building up to service speed when it was noticed that we had a singing blade on the starboard propeller which was a controllable pitch designed and supplied by Stones. The ship returned to the mouth of the Tyne and experts flew up from London. Once on board, the rest of Saturday night we ranged up and down the coast while expert opinions were given by a variety of people on causes and effects. The result of deliberations was that we returned to the yard early on Sunday, the dry-dock being available, we entered and commenced drying out. You can imagine the surprise and relief of Stones when it

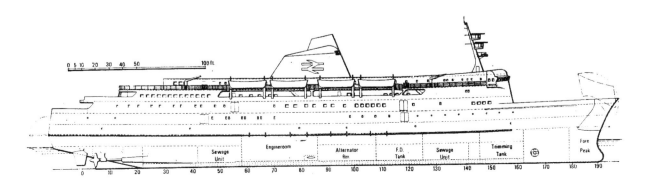

St George (Jim Ashby collection)

was seen that a paint drum had impacted on to the leading edge of the suspect blade, probably during dockside engine trials. It was hosed off and that was the end of the problem.

It was interesting to be on board the *St. George* one night when preparing to leave the berth at the Hook of Holland.

The ship had arrived in the Hook and berthed bow up the river on the north bank and had to cross over to the south side of the river on leaving to pick up the outward bound stream of traffic.

With a very busy river having both deep-sea, coasting and local river traffic in both the incoming and outgoing streams of traffic it could be quite hazardous when the tide was running out at a fast rate.

Don had been attending a meeting at the Hook at which discussion had taken place on manoeuvring and was on the bridge when the *St. George* was ready to depart. It was a clear but dark night and traffic was heavy in both directions with a lot of traffic running with the outgoing tide. We were singled up for 40 minutes before there was a safe gap to swing, cross the river, and join the outward bound ships.

The *St. George* was our first and only seagoing ship with a completely enclosed bridge and it was a big step forward for us. Discussion had raged over the years about closed and open bridge wings. We use the word "raged" advisedly as the debates had been quite heated at times.

However common sense won at last and we designed a fully enclosed bridge. All equipment could then be designed for best use inside without the necessity for wind and weather shields. We attempted to give the best visibility we could and fitted Therglass heated panels in all the forward facing windows to reduce

condensation. These were a success in that condensation was much reduced but the fitting of the windows was not perfect. The wheelhouse, being 72 ft. from wing to wing and of fairly light construction was subject to structural movement and, when heated on cold windy nights, the window panels tended to break and craze and were eventually taken out.

We made one elementary mistake in the fitting out of the bridge in that we did not initially fit an opening window in the forward face at the outer ends and this was first criticised by the River Pilots when departing the shipyard for trials. They would not or could not use walkie-talkie radios and insisted on being able to shout and whistle to the tug masters. This was taken up by the opposition to closed bridges and except for the I.O.W. ferries we never fitted another. A small error that was quickly corrected led us backwards for years.

It was interesting some years later when we had discussions during the design of the *St. Edmund* that at a meeting attended by all available sea going staff, every one who had served on the bridge in the *St. George*

Main car deck - **St George** *(Jim Ashby collection)*

recommended a fully closed bridge for the new ship and everyone who had not been on the *St. George* was on the side of an open bridge. To our regret, the open bridge won.

The *St. George* had an interesting design for the hoistable mezzanine car decks. Every panel could be hoisted up to the deckhead to leave the space clear for high vehicles but as there was a frequent variation in the number of cars and high vehicles carried, we had to devise a method of using one or more panels for two levels of cars without the necessity of having to lower all panels either for loading or discharging as happens when you have ramps only at the ends.

We decided to make every panel into a double acting ramp and MacGregors' designed them with a sort of plumb blob suspension. When the panel was lowered in its guides, it lowered equally to mezzanine deck level and then, with the support pins at one end removed, the panel could ramp down to the main deck. This gave us total flexibility on the number of panels in use at any one time with no delays for loading or discharging and it was a very simple and easy to use system. As far as we know the system has not been used again.

To be able to accommodate other European services at the Ro-Ro ramp in Parkeston Quay, it was decided to depart from the usual B.R. practice and use the ships' end doors as vehicle ramps between the end of the main deck and the shore bridge.

The *St. George* had the first of the new funnels that became generic on Sealink ships and was the result of intensive smoke tests in the research department at Swan Hunter's being extremely effective in reducing smoke and oily smut levels on the after decks. She was also the first of the ships with the main engine room and alternator room separated by a compartment containing the machinery control room.

1968   SEA FREIGHTLINER I and
          SEA FREIGHTLINER II

Our design of these two container ships was literally 'from a clean sheet of paper' with no precedents to guide us. We even had to assist in the design of cast container fittings including novel

hatch cover fittings which could be changed in position to accommodate various lengths of containers. The movable guide system in the holds was another first, an intricate bolted cell structure to take a mix of container sizes to suit traffic on offer.

Tony had the honour, shortly after the service commenced, of escorting Prince Philip on a tour of the *Sea Freightliner I* at Parkeston Quay. Having just explained the principle of standard ISO units, 8 feet x 8 feet width and height, to Tony's embarrassment His Royal Highness pointed to a container very obviously projecting above the others in one cell. The likelihood of higher containers had, in fact, been foreseen and the ships were designed for this future contingency.

After placing the order for the twin ships with Readhead's yard in North Shields, a change in hatch cover and hold design necessitated an extra two feet being added to the ships' length. A small and very reasonable increase in cost was consequently agreed.

However at the same time it had been decided that twin rudders should be adopted (tenders allowed for single or twin rudders, optional). The effect of their incorporation was that the statutory measurement of length was reduced by precisely two feet! The 'between perpendiculars' length of the ships was thus reduced to the originally specified dimension. Throughout the period of building, Tony took great delight in asking his old friend George Atkins (Readhead's Naval Architect) for his money back!

These two ships were the first European designed, built and owned cellular container ships and were built specifically to handle the liner traffic in ISO containers. This was building up especially by Ford's between their car manufacturing plants in the U.K. and near Continent and based on the newly built terminals in Parkeston Quay and Zeebrugge.

They were also the first ships for B.R. that had a diesel driven bow thrust unit, the exhaust of which was up the forward mast. This gave us problems as in Zeebrugge, containers were often fleeted along the quay by the transporter cranes rather than directly traversed on to the quay and frequent contact was made with the upper portion of the mast until we eventually hinged the top sections to avoid the collisions.

The cargo holds were divided into nominal 60 ft. long main cells with the cellular guide system designed to be movable in the 60 ft. length to accommodate 40, 30 and 20 ft. I.S.O. containers.

The hatch covers were of innovative 'piggy-back' design by MacGregor's and were of deep pontoon type, each alternate cover being powered by a chain drive along each side coaming and sliding under the intermediate covers which were raised clear by hydraulic jacks, lowered on to the powered pontoons and rolled along the coamings to reveal the whole 60 ft. cell. Two complete cells were available for load or discharge by the two cranes on the quay. The covers were also stiffened to take a full load of containers and had pots to accept virtually any mix of 40, 30, 20 or 10 ft. I.S.O. units.

The two ships were also the first where we fitted a protected escape trunk from the engine room floor level to the open deck with a fire door at the foot and a steel hatch immediately forward of the bridge front.

1969 VORTIGERN

This rail ferry, destined for Dover/ Dunkerque service, had a chequered career before she was built. Don did the first design general arrangement in 1958 before it was deferred as the chance of a Channel Tunnel arose and was resurrected when the tunnel proposals receded. This went on for eight or nine years and Don must have produced at least fifteen different designs as commercial and operating managers were changed and ideas altered. Some were for four track decks, some three track, some five track and with single centre casings, twin ship's side casings and even with twin offset casings. Eventually the service could not cope with the 1934/ 5 built ferries and an order was placed with Swan Hunter for the new ship.

The arrangement of public rooms on the *Vortigern* was very poor. A rational arrangement had been agreed with the commercial and operating departments when our Operations Manager, John Bustard, decided that he did not like it and a whole new scheme with a series of small public rooms some with reclining seats for overnight foot passengers from the sleeper trains was bodged together to suit his requirements The whole arrangement was a disaster and led to a series of modifications over the years, particularly in bars and shops although the cafeteria forward was modified once or twice.

The ship was delivered with a steward service restaurant at the forward end but we do not know that it was ever used as such except for special parties and some years later a portion was partitioned off as a crew mess room.

The *Vortigern* was the first aptly named multi-purpose ship carrying trains and/ or Ro-Ro and cars on the main deck, cars on mezzanine deck and at the upper garage level where the cars were loaded directly into the side of the ship via

a short ramp in each of the train ferry berths: portside at Dover, starboard at Dunkerque.

The cargo access gear was designed and provided by Cargospeed and had some interesting features.

The mezzanine deck panels immediately forward of the after ramp sections had a piggy-back arrangement with ramp panels in the deck of the upper garage enabling the upper level to be loaded and discharged by bow or stern doors with vehicles traversing the upper ramps to mezzanine deck level and then down the mezzanine ramps to main deck. This was used very little and the upper garage was eventually turned into an additional passenger lounge. The stern door was an unusual design as it jack-knifed upwards and was pinned into the horizontal at the upper garage deck level to enable cars to be loaded at a two level shore ramp. To our knowledge this method of loading the upper garage was never used.

The bow also had its adventures. On train ferry duty, the ship was only loaded and discharged via the stern and the bow door and visor were left closed for the periods of duty on Dover/ Dunkerque. Being a train ferry, buffers were required for the ends of the four tracks. Outboard tracks were no problem as casings were available to attach substantial buffers but for the centre tracks we had to make portable buffers available. The eventual arrangement was a large movable horizontal beam, substantially buttressed at each end which lay in the buffer position for train service and was attached by wires to the downward hinging bow door. The beam acted as a balance weight as the door was opened, sliding upwards to a space under the deckhead clear of the high vehicles.

The width of the bow door was always a problem for Ro-Ro on the *Vortigern*. A much wider door had originally been specified and, as this was the first Sealink bow door ship to be proposed for Boulogne, we had long discussions with the Chambre de Commerce on the details. It was agreed at our early meetings that the ship would lay alongside the berth with no firm nesting contact with the 'shoe' piles as was being quite successfully done in Stranraer with the *Antrim Princess*. Then there was a change in the

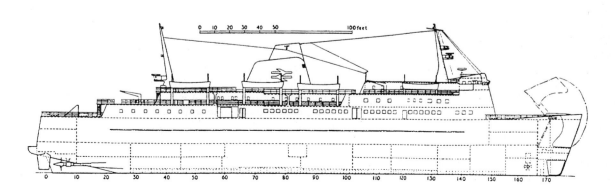

Boulogne requirements for the ship to have firm contact with the piles. We reduced the proposed width of the bow door and visor opening and at the same time substantially stiffened up the shoulders of the shell in way of the visor openings. This was to maintain contact with the shoe piles, with the end of the bow door entered a little way between the closest piles.

However when we took the ship in to Boulogne for port trials we were *then* told we had to stand the ship at least a metre further aft so that the bow door, when down, was clear of the piles. We then had to fit a 'cow catcher' at the stem below the visor to hold the ship in position. All this, after sacrificing a proper width of bow opening to suit local requirements which then changed.

We had fun at Dunkerque with the stern too. When the ship was being built, the old train ferry *Shepperton Ferry* was in Swan's on refit. Opportunity was taken to make a full template of the rail ends at the stern to enable a good fit at Dover and Dunkerque. The shore bridge fitted on to the stern apron, about 2 ft. 6 inches below main deck level, and was locked in position by sitting over a rounded top 7 inch square pin secured into the transom structure. The shipyard worker who had lined off the socket for the pin had taken the wrong side of the longitudinal plate girder as centreline and the bridge sat on the pin 7/16" out. This was not a lot but, much to the amusement of our French colleagues, was sufficient to prevent the rail pawls dropping in during port trials at Dunkerque. The pin was removed, skimmed on one side, packed and replaced with then a perfect fit.

Some time later the sterns on two of the Harwich train ferries were cut back finer, about 2 metres taken off each side, to enable them to run to Dunkerque. The Harwich and Zeebrugge shore bridges had extended side girders which landed on large pads on the ship's stern with the locating pin standing well above main deck level. This pin had to be made portable and was removed before the ship entered the Dunkerque terminal. On one occasion the pin on the *Essex Ferry*, a 7 inch square 3ft long piece of steel, was trapped in the shore bridge as it lifted and dropped into the water as the ship left. While the *Vortigern* was being built, swift advances were being made in the computer calculation of damaged stability and it was discovered that in some intermediate flooding conditions, she would not survive. This prompted some cross flooding ducts to be fitted in the ship which obviated the problems.

At the same time, a series of tests in open water were being run at Feltham with a model of the *Holyhead Ferry I*. In one of the tests, to simulate a side damage a vee section was triggered out of the side of the

model in way of the machinery spaces. However, as the water rushed in the impact rolled the model away from the damage and she remained afloat with the aperture above the resultant waterline. There was immediate consternation in the minds of the Department of Transport Surveyors while others who were present, including Don, thought of re-writing Attwood, the 'bible' to many budding naval architects, and in whose pages this just could not happen.

However this was only one of a series of tests and experiments which lead to fairly fundamental changes in design to ensure that problems did not arise on future ships in the intermediate flooding conditions.

The *Vortigern* was designed to be able to carry the Wagon-Lits night ferry sleeping cars on their journey between London/ Paris and Brussels. Open sewage troughs were fitted between the rails with salt water flushing arrangements and hinged covers.

The Wagon-Lits carriages were still equipped with anthracite-burning stoves to supply heating and hot water for the cabin wash basins and much horror was expressed by the Department of Transport at the prospect of these being alight on the train deck of a passenger ship. We overcame this by two means. First the stoves were damped down with moist fuel and little draught before they were put on to the ship. Secondly, and as further precaution to prevent fire spreading from the Wagon-Lits to road vehicles or vice-versa, additional lines of drencher heads were fitted to provide a curtain of water between the inner rail tracks and the outer lanes of Ro-Ro or cars.

When the *Vortigern* was on port trials John Arthur, later Commodore of the Sealink fleet, brought the ship stern first into the terminal in

Vortigern *(John Hendy)*

Dover at the usual rate of knots. It was noticeable that as the stern approached the berth a collection of shipyard personnel looking over the rails above the after mooring deck stepped smartly away from the rails anticipating an almighty crash as the ship hit the berth. They had not realised how Capt. Arthur was using the cushion of water to rapidly slow the ship and ease her gently into the shoe.

John Hendy

1969   CUTHRED

This was the first of the 'modern' ferries for the Isle of Wight services and was the model for the later series headed by the *Caedmon* in 1973. The ship was launched by Tony's wife, Kathleen.

A new underwater shape of rounded form in lieu of the hard chine form of previous ships was specially designed by Tony and the horsepower required was reduced by about 30%. One disadvantage appeared on trials when it was discovered that the ship would spin quite well to port but more slowly to starboard as the water flow from the Voith Schneider propellers was impeded from passing the steeper sided end sponsons. Large rounded notches were cut at each end and the problem was overcome with steering and turning back to normal.

Centre casings were fitted and a good drive through arrangement was possible. This was our first visit to Richards' in Lowestoft.

One problem that persisted throughout our careers was that railway-trained management could not appreciate the extremely high costs of unnecessarily high ship speed. One additional knot adds about 25% to engine power and fuel consumption. Technical arguments that the service speed of the *Cuthred* should not be higher than the 9 knots of the existing ferries were of no avail until a letter appeared in an Isle of Wight newspaper.

The letter praised the efficiency and courtesy of ships' staff who offered a car wash service on passage! The writer had observed that on approaching Fishbourne, the deck crew signalled to the bridge that they had not quite finished. On receipt of the signal the ferry was stopped whilst the deck crew applied the finishing touches to the writer's car after which a second signal enabled the ferry to berth. We wonder if the correspondent appreciated that his car was being washed with salt water!

Whilst the much improved hull form of the *Cuthred* enabled her to carry 50% more passengers and cars than her predecessors using the same propulsive horsepower, she proved to be a 'fair-weather' ferry. Her 'windage' area above the waterline slowed her down in gale conditions and her *Caedmon* class 'sisters which followed were fitted with increased power to overcome this problem.

An interesting proposal for further use for *Cuthred* after she was eventually withdrawn from service was as a 'people mover' in Dover Harbour. At that time proposals were being examined to transfer foot passengers from the Marine Station to the Eastern Docks to obviate the ferries berthing at the Western Docks to coincide with Boat Trains. We suggested that *Cuthred* could be used as a cross-harbour ferry between the dockside at the Marine Station and the outboard side of ferries berthed in Eastern Docks. By either premonition or coincidence, the upper deck of the *Cuthred* was almost exactly on the level of the main shell doors on *St. Anselm* and could provide easy and safe access for passengers transferring between the vessels. The proposal was evaluated but was not finally acceptable.

Jim Ashby collection

1970   BRIAN BOROIME and
RHODRI MAWR

Built in Cobh in Eire these ships were substantially the same as the 'Sea Freightliners' but larger in beam and one bay of containers shorter in length. They were designed to run a three port service between Holyhead and Dublin and Holyhead and Belfast.

The hatch covers were designed and supplied by Cargo Dynamics with a new and sophisticated mechanism for hatch movement but as the firm went out of business before the ships were completed, the shipyard engaged MacGregor's to complete the work and commission the installation.

The mechanics of building ships in Verolme Cork Dockyard were complicated as most of the plans, specifications and orders for equipment etc. and the technical meetings were carried out in the Verolme yards at either Isselmunde or Alblasserdam and with the electrical department in Maasluis in Holland.

Typical Irish hospitality was a distinct advantage and one of the team met his future wife there.

Ailsa Princess (FotoFlite)

1971 AILSA PRINCESS

This was our first new ship built in continental Europe. Designed as an improved *Antrim Princess*, the order was placed with Breda in Venice. It was interesting from day one.

We had no ongoing reputation with Breda and needed to convince them that what we had drawn out and specified was the best for the purpose.

The Technical Manager led a team of highly competent and questioning personnel and we had many discussions on methods, procedures and details. It was also our introduction to the Italian public room outfitters, Cantrisa of Trieste, who did a great job on the ship by carrying out Ward and Austin designs to a high standard of finish.

The main engines were Crossley Pielstick as were those on the *Antrim Princess* and the ship taking them out broke down off Portugal. B.R. had to put money on the table to guarantee payments of salvage claims before the ship was able to proceed after repairs.

Breda were not satisfied with the profile of the ship and we eventually compromised and allowed them to fit extensions to the B.R. logo making it look as if it extended right round the funnel and suspending the after mast at the forward end of the logo. On one occasion Tony was followed to Venice airport by the yard's Technical Manager who had eight different models for proposed funnel designs.

The material for the majority of the structural fire protection insulation on this ship was agreed as Stillite but soon after the order was placed, the Department of Transport withdrew their approval and we had to find an alternative quickly but no delay resulted.

At the suggestion of the shipyard, the *Ailsa Princess* was fitted with Sperry stabilisers manufactured in Italy. When the ship took up service it was discovered that a component had been fitted 90 degrees out of phase and the ship rolled heavier with the fins out. This was quickly corrected.

Due to international licensing agreements we could not fit AEG rotary vane steering gear manufactured by Brown Bros. to ensure compatibility with spares on the *Antrim Princess* and this resulted in the Donkin gear being supplied.

Small items can cause great upsets. When the technical manager of the Breda shipyard, Amadeo Caporaletti, passed through the control room on the *Ailsa Princess* to help to sort out a problem with the Graviner oil mist detectors in the main engine room, he noticed that the pipe fitters had penetrated the deckhead lining of the control room and left a short section of painted pipe in full view. He nearly "went through the roof", recriminations were loud, long and forcible and the pipe was moved. The problem in the engine room had to wait.

1972 HENGIST and HORSA

At the time that these ships were being designed, B.R. had a programme for no fewer than five new passenger/ vehicle ships: the first was for Holyhead, the second for Fishguard, third for Newhaven and numbers four and five were for Dover.

In the event, due to the competition, the two Dover ships were put at the head of the queue.

M. Graf, the head of our French partners in Sealink was a long time friend of the Admiral in charge of the naval dockyard in Brest and he suggested we should invite the Dockyard to tender. We did and accepted their tender for the two ships while a later option was signed up for the Newhaven/ Dieppe ship *Senlac*.

The *Hengist* and *Horsa* were designed during 1969, once again under the shadow of an

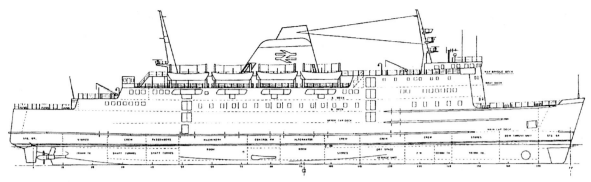

impending Channel Tunnel, and we had to incorporate features that would allow sensible commercial use on another B.R. route. The required vehicle capacity more or less decided the size of ship but the layout of the space was designed to be modified for use on Heysham/Belfast to replace the 'Dukes' when the Dover ships were made redundant because of the tunnel. The twin, offset, machinery and stair casings in the vehicle deck allowed two lanes of Ro-Ro in the centre and one each outboard of the casings. In the Heysham alternative the portable mezzanine decks outboard of the casings were to be removed, a permanent deck fitted for the length of the vehicle deck and the new spaces at the mezzanine level fitted out as comfortable lounges with reclining seats for the night sailings.

The main deck side areas were to remain as single height spaces for cars only, leaving the centre section for Ro-Ro or two levels of cars. The ships were also fitted with an astern wheelhouse and bridge to enable the practice of entering Belfast astern to continue. This was at considerable cost of equipment, space and duplication of controls and quite unjustifiable in our opinion. Some of the masters used the after bridge when proceeding astern into the berth but

a better view of the quayside was obtained from the forward wings where the movement of the ship sideways could be judged. The *Hengist* and *Horsa* were extremely manoeuvrable and did not need stern bridges.

Needless to say the *Horsa* ran her last trip from Folkestone to Boulogne on 31st December 1991, well before the date for the opening of the tunnel, and a real swell of old salts were on board too.

The two ships were built in dry-dock in Brest nose to tail, two months apart in progress but named in double ceremony while floating at the quayside on a day that was extremely wet even by Brest standards.

Being a naval yard they had their own construction and fitting-out standards but the details of public accommodation work we required were well above their warship standards and had to be detailed with extreme care to achieve the desired results.

Their electrical and mechanical detail was excellent and no detail that was not already familiar to them went unchallenged.

One department that we have never seen equalled was the co-ordination drawing office, where every detail was accurately transferred to

Hengist and *Horsa* (FotoFlite)

Above: **Southsea**
(John Hendy)
Below: **Camber Queen**
(John Hendy)

composite co-ordination plans for every area of the ship and these plans were strictly adhered to. So strictly that when, because of the development, or change in requirements, an item needed to be changed on the first ship, the second ship was taken to the same stage to allow an identical change to be made in accordance with the plans.

The French yard learnt a lot from us in the fitting out of the ships and we certainly appreciated their attention to detail.

We also appreciated the splendid lunches we had in the Cercle Navale, the officers' club in Brest.

The method of delegation in the yard was interesting. We had a lot of meetings in the early part of the contract and on each occasion separate teams of technical personnel would appear, lead by a uniformed officer in charge of his section. The teams varied from a minimum of three to up to eight or nine. Each team would discuss with us the development and details in their discipline and take full responsibility for their section. Co-ordination between the teams was carried out separately without us being present.

The contract for public room outfitting was won by Cantrisa and an excellent standard was produced.

In the design of the public spaces, Don had been asked to provide a space for a major mural and the forward main stairs were designed to have a two deck space where this could be fitted in on each ship.

The murals were designed by the artist Franta Belsky and excited much comment over the years, some of it derogatory.

Much to our surprise the French Dockyard asked if Sealink personnel could do the catering on board for the trials. This was agreed for the first two ships, the cream of the Dover catering staff were flown out and we out Frenched the French in scope of menu and quality of food. The crew were quite upset that normal service on the ship did not allow for such splendid multi-course meals.

When interrogated at the entrance to the French Naval Dockyard in Brest by a surly French official, Don gave his father's and mother's names as William Ripley and Elizabeth Ripley. The official looked surprised and questioned, "The same name?". Don replied, "*my* parents were married." It did not do him any good, it still took ten minutes for each person to gain an official dockyard pass.

Under Sea Containers directions, both ships had large areas of their public spaces refitted in readiness for the Orient Express cross Channel link. Jenny McClean, the interior design architect for the modifications took great interest in the pictures that were displayed on the bulkheads. These had been selected by Neville Ward and Frank Austin as part of their remit for the original decorative schemes but Jenny was excited to see that one of the 'works of art' was by none other than the celebrated artist Dame Elizabeth Frink. By 1986 she had become rather better known than in 1972 when the ships were completed and the value of the picture had increased enormously.

1973   SENLAC

The third ship in the series from Brest was completed a year after the *Hengist* and *Horsa* for the Newhaven/ Dieppe service and ran under the U.K. flag. The joint service between Newhaven and Dieppe had been set up with two-thirds French capital and one-third U.K. Sealink capital and the French insisted on a considerable say in the layout of the public spaces. This was eventually confined to the catering areas on the upper passenger deck and a radically different arrangement of cafeteria, galley, and restaurant resulted.

1973   ST. EDMUND

Again we had long discussions with our Dutch colleagues to enable the *St. Edmund* to be built to fit into the fleet pattern for the Parkeston Quay/ Hook service. The order was placed with Cammell Laird for delivery in May 1973 but as normal with U.K. yards at that time, all kinds of problems meant the ship was seven months late and delivered only just in time for Christmas.

The *St. Edmund* was a very good ship but

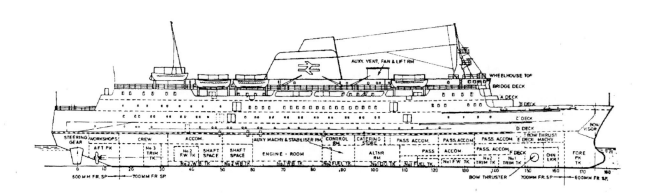

FotoFlite

When the ship was completed, an oversize ball was fitted by the yard in one of the Winel airvalves to the double bottom tanks. The airpipe to a fresh water tank was severely restricted and the double bottom plating was set up when the tank was filled.

The ship eventually got away from Birkenhead but had to put into Rotterdam for a dry-docking to replace a faulty component in the starboard controllable pitch propeller.

Some may remember that the ship was requisitioned by the M.O.D. for use in the Falklands war and was used extensively as an accommodation ship being known locally as the Stanley Hilton.

hampered with shipyard problems. The fitting out took place while Ted Heath's infamous three day week was in force but you could not notice the difference in progress. A hand painted notice in the ship carried the legend "Vote for Ted, Four days in bed." The ship was fitted with Stork Werkspoor main engines.

To reduce the possibility of noise and vibration in the accommodation above machinery and propellers, we decided to fit what was then defined as a floating deck which consisted of a heavy multi-layer composition manufactured and laid by Durastic. The composition was about 65 mm. thick, laid from steel bulkhead to steel bulkhead with the grounds for partitions secured to the surface. We had a hard time convincing the Department of Transport that it was a sensible arrangement but as the composition obtained an 'A' Class certificate it was a very good solution and most successful.

While the St. Edmund was fitting-out, we had the first meaningful discussions on the use of non-asbestos board for linings and partitions. Asbestos was becoming an apparent problem and all working of Marinite boards had to be carried out in a dust booth in the joiners' shop with waste properly disposed of. Both Cape and Turners were working on new boards and the eventual result was Capeboard, an asbestos-free board generally in use now.

On her being taken up for service, Eddie Robson, who had supervised the St. Edmund's building, was despatched by Tony to Devonport dockyard without pyjamas or toothbrush to assist in her preparation. Eddie was later to superintend, on behalf of the M.O.D., her modifications on return from the Falklands when she was sold to the M.O.D.and renamed Keren.

FotoFlite

1973   CAEDMON, CENWULF and CENRED

These three sister ships were built by Robb Caledon at Dundee for the passenger and vehicle services between Portsmouth and Fishbourne (Caedmon) and Lymington and Yarmouth. Although based largely on the Cuthred they had enlarged public spaces to cater for the greater

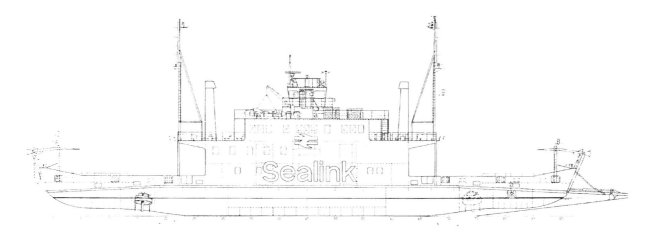

Senlac (Ferry Publications Library)

Horsa *(FotoFlite)*

Saint Eloi (FotoFlite)

number of passengers: 756 as against the 400 on the earlier design. Vehicle capacity was also increased by the fitting of portable car decks soon after they were in service and the *Cuthred* returned to her builders in Lowestoft for the same additional capacity.

As Class IV ships, these craft were not required to be fitted to any degree with structural fire protection but what was done on the *Cuthred* was extended on these three ships with protected stairways from vehicle decks to the passenger accommodation and outside escape ladders for emergencies.

A series of side shell doors, hydraulically operated were fitted port and starboard in the passenger stairways to allow passenger access to the sloping quays at Lymington and Yarmouth at all states of the tide.

1975 SAINT ELOI

The Dover/Dunkerque train ferry service was operated by four ships and the *Saint Eloi* was to be the replacement for the *Twickenham Ferry*, the last in service of the 1934/5 generation. This ship had been under the management of the joint company Alsace-Lorraine-Angleterre and sailed under the French flag although the company was

80% B.R. and 20% S.N.C.F. When the new ship was proposed it was agreed that a copy of the *Vortigern* was the answer and the French obtained tenders and placed the order in Italy with Pietro-Ligure. Delivery should have been about May 1972 coinciding with the *Hengist* but, due to all sorts of problems, the ship was not finally delivered until March 1975.

It was decided in the design stage that as it was the intention to retain the ship on the rail service, it was not necessary to fit bow access or portable mezzanine car decks.

Thus, although provision was made for their fitting in the distant future, neither bow visor nor inner bow door were fitted but some provision was made for future portable decks. The upper garage was fitted-out to take cars but with side access only.

As 80% owners, Sealink insisted that the ship be built to comply with Department of Transport regulations to safeguard possible future use in the U.K. The vessel sails today as the Isle of Man Steam Packet Company's, *King Orry*.

1977   ST. COLUMBA

This was to be the last of the passenger/vehicle ferries with the main deck strong enough

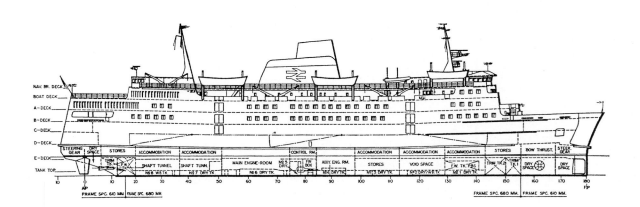

St Columba (Miles Cowsill)

to carry 35 tonne vehicles but with insufficient deadweight to carry a full deck load of fully laden Ro-Ro. It was a traditional passenger/ car ferry built with a Ro-Ro capability to cope with the expected commercial traffic requirements.

The order was placed with Aalborg and discussions commenced with their highly competent technical team. One significant difference we found with Aalborg was that the major subcontracts were placed much sooner than with a U.K. yard. This had the advantage of the subcontractor for such items as air conditioning being able to collaborate with the yard in the development of the systems which was both sensible and economical. This also enabled rapid progress to be made in the development of the structural and outfitting arrangements.

With a nominal passenger capacity of 2,400, 39 more than the *Hibernia* which had the previous highest passenger certificate, we had serious problems in finding space for the required life saving appliances. We had discussions with the D.O.T. and eventually submitted proposals that although did not strictly comply with the U.K. Regulations were fully in keeping with SOLAS principles and considered by the Department as very logical and safe, fully meeting their evacuation requirements. Very large motor lifeboats and davit-launched inflatable rafts were fitted accommodate all persons on board with the usual 25 per cent spare capacity. In addition, two semi-rigid permanently inflated rescue boats were fitted taking the place of the normal smaller capacity rigid motor lifeboats fitted for rescue purposes.

These new type boats were in excess of the required life saving appliances for evacuation and were fitted under gravity davits to act both as fast rescue boats and as additional marshalling boats for the inflatable rafts.

Stairways were also a major headache in the *St. Columba* as with 2,400 persons on board, vast staircases were required to enable all persons to reach the embarkation stations.

When designing the *St. Columba*, little attention was given to the possibility of duty-free shopping which had been for years a pipe dream on the Irish Services.

However, before the ship had been in service for a year, a decision was rushed through by the U.K. and Irish Governments to allow duty free-trade on the services between U.K. and Eire. Modifications to public rooms less than a year old were rapidly put in hand as we only had six weeks between the announcement and the opening of duty free trade. A combined 1st and 2nd Class shop was fitted, with access via the galley lift to a liquor store on the tank top spaces forward which were rearranged for the purpose.

Trade rapidly overtook the capacity of the shops and at the same time it was decided to go one class on the route. This gave us an opportunity to fit a larger shop aft and turnover increased considerably. As the emphasis on sales has altered, so the shop was later altered with major modifications taking place twice in the basic layout and content of the shops.

A casino was established in part of the second class bar when the ship was built and it proved extremely popular with the sporting clientele.

The *St. Columba* was the only ship that really needed an after bridge and it was extensively used for astern navigation when leaving the berth at the head of the harbour in Holyhead and proceeding out to open water before being able to turn and run ahead. Frydenbo steering gear was fitted on this ship.

In the design and layout of the public spaces, a lot of thought was given to the problem of feeding the largest possible number of passengers with a reasonable meal. The catering department

Above: **Earl Granville**
(FotoFlite)
Below: **Cambridge Ferry**
(FotoFlite)

did a lot of research and eventually we arranged to fit a carousel system with a very sophisticated back-up. Food was cooked in conventional ways, full meals were plated up ready to serve, these were then blast chilled and placed in cooled storage. When these were required, selections of meals were brought out on special trolleys that fitted directly into Regi-Thermic ovens where the food was heated rapidly without additional cooking. This allowed meals to be prepared on a steady basis round the clock and brought out in large quantities when demand was at its highest. It was the first example on a ship but unfortunately was not made to work correctly and was eventually taken out.

An excellent relationship was built up with Aalborg especially as the ship was delivered fully completed two months early.

When designing the *St. Columba* many discussions took place with the civil engineers in B.R. about the terminal design and the necessary modifications to the existing facilities at Holyhead which were not capable of accepting such a large ship. One item that astonished us was that at a meeting to discuss progress of the terminal, the B.R. civil engineers demanded three months for a rough estimate +/- 30% and six months for a firm estimate +/- 10% for the cost of the buildings to house H.M. Customs, H.M. Immigration and reception facilities for passengers in both in and out directions. We thought they were joking as Tony would give an estimate for a totally new ship or major conversion in a couple of hours and be more accurate every time than +/- 10%.

1980   GALLOWAY PRINCESS

The *Galloway Princess* was the culmination of four or five years design work on a new generation of ships. We had been asked by the commercial and operating departments to design a 'standard' Ro-Ro carrier that could fit the majority of Sealink ports both in the U.K. and at the outer ends of the routes. We had a requirement for 650 to 700 linear metres of Ro-Ro space, decks capable of taking heavy axle loads and a deadweight capacity capable of carrying a full deck load of Ro-Ro up to a high average weight.

Passenger capacity was not defined at that early stage but was left to be decided by the route operators.

The ships had to be capable of being loaded at both Ro-Ro deck levels directly from a double level shore bridge with bow and stern access. A request was made that the majority of vehicles should be able to be driven directly into their travelling positions with no manoeuvring.

We also had the requirement, which was onerous in view of the last request, that the ship should be able to load and discharge a full load of vehicles at a single level shore bridge where no double level was available.

To enable vehicles to transfer from one deck to another whether it be upwards or downwards there are two options: ramps or lifts. We examined various combinations of lifts, some with 2 x 12 metre vehicles in line and some with up to 6 x 12 metre vehicles. None could approach the speed of transfer required to allow a full load to be discharged and the ship fully loaded again in the initial target of 75 minutes.

With the fertile brain of Jack Brown, the head of Cargospeed, the Clyde-based designer and manufacturer of cargo access equipment, we drew out tentative proposals for the upper level to be almost wholly a movable deck tilting down at either end to be able to load or discharge from forward or aft. This was an extremely heavy proposal both in weight of the ramping deck and associated equipment and the structure to support the ramp and the huge aperture in the upper Ro-Ro deck and was eventually discarded as impractical.

Proposals for ramps were drawn out time and again but with an optimum slope for rapid transit of heavy lorries of not more than 1 in 8 and vertical transfer of about 6 metres between decks, it was impossible in the length of the ship to have single direction ramps in association with two horizontal and parallel decks.

Don then doodled about with ideas to shorten the ramps and evolved the solution you can see in the *Galloway Princess* generation of ships and since used on many other Ro-Ro carriers. It was simple when drawn out. Lower the hinge points of the back to back ramps and raise the contact point with the deck below. After a few attempts with different slopes, lengths and positions, he was able to draw out proposals for the series of ramps which were eventually fitted and these proposals met two very important criteria for the ship. Every vehicle could be driven directly into the travelling position and this could be done, using the ramps, from a single or a double level shore bridge.

Great scepticism was levelled at the first proposals drawn out but as they were examined it dawned on us that we had a great solution and we went ahead with the specification of details. MacGregor's obtained the contract for the cargo access gear and supplied both the bow and stern access doors visors etc. and the four large ramps, each of which was designed to be raised or lowered carrying six loaded Ro-Ro vehicles. The method of raising and lowering was by chains over large chain sprocket wheels and although we had a few problems when overload tests were carried out on the ship, with sparks flying and chains jerking, these were overcome with correct lubrication of the chains.

We had a minor problem with the fire protection in these vehicle spaces. The SOLAS Regulations, formulated some years before,

Galloway Princess (Miles Cowsill)

allowed the special category spaces one above the other to be considered one space for fire protection purposes if their combined height was not more than 10 metres. The clear height for vehicles on two levels plus the sloped decks did not enable the combined height to be contained within the 10 metres and the DOT required a fire barrier to be fitted at the boundaries of the four ramps. We were able to satisfy their requirements by a steel labyrinth similar to that used on sliding fire doors to prevent passage of smoke and flame. As an aside we immediately drew out a submission to the DOT to request the IMO to consider alterations to the special category space height limitations.

We pointed out that the original intention of the SOLAS Regulations was to allow two levels of Ro-Ro in one overall space and Tony, who was on the subcommittee that drew out those proposals, confirmed that it was he that proposed the 10 metre figure increased from the 8 metres originally suggested by the IMO Secretariat. We further pointed out that with ships getting larger in beam and with many ships having no centre casings to split the span, the beams supporting the deck over both spaces (particularly the beams supporting the upper Ro-Ro deck) were in some ships at least one metre deep. With the clear height requirement of up to 5 metres on each deck, the SOLAS Regulations were now being overtaken.

We suggested that the DOT should propose to the IMO that the height limitation should be increased to either 12 metres between decks or allow a combined clear height of 10 metres. We were pleased that the Department eventually fully supported our arguments based on the fact that we were not proposing an extra fire load as the additional height was required for structure. This was supported by the Marine Safety Committee at their next meeting and the SOLAS Regulations were altered to allow special category spaces to contain two levels provided the combined clear height for vehicles did not exceed 10 metres. We were then able to discard the steel labyrinths at the perimeters of the ramps.

Normally on a Sealink ferry we specified that the exhaust ventilation for the vehicle decks should be 600 cubic feet/ car/ min. based on a full load of cars and this had been found satisfactory to dissipate the fumes from Ro – Ro also. In this ship we had only one level of cars per deck and we had to re-evaluate our requirements. The exhaust ventilation on the *St. Columba* based on the 600 cubic feet/ car/ min. criteria and with two levels of cars gave a figure of 33.6 changes of air per hour when calculated using the volume of the whole vehicle space on the *St. Columba*. We then specified 35 changes of air per hour exhaust ventilation for the *Galloway Princess* series of ships with supply ventilation partly by the open access doors at the loading or discharge end of the space and partly by supply vents blasting air into the space.

The *Galloway Princess* was originally specified and ordered to carry 600 passengers but Tony persuaded the Sealink management in the design stages to fit toilet spaces, life saving appliances and services capable for a total of 1,000 persons to allow for future growth. Traffic figures on the existing ship were increasing as the ship was ordered and it was soon decided that at completion she should have a passenger certificate of 1,000.

When designing the underwater form, the operators in Stranraer were asked whether they required a bow rudder or a more fuel efficient bulbous bow. When we tank tested in St. Albans and David Moor's diamond shaped bulb showed 11% economy of power over the form with a bow rudder, the immediate preference was for a bulb and this was fitted.

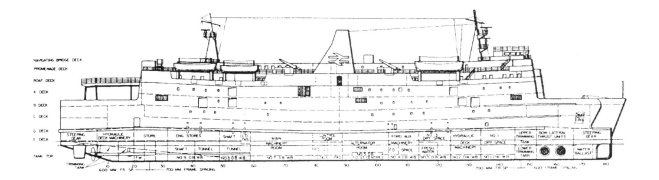

Harland and Wolff proposed to us that we should fit hydraulic deck machinery. We had examined proposals for previous ships but no supplier had been able to meet our demand of concurrent use of three or four capstans or winches at random loads of anywhere between light rope and full load. The yard suggested we should discuss our requirements with Kocks of Bremen and they confirmed that with their systems of ring main and swash plate pumps switching in on demand, we could get exactly what we required. We visited the factory and were impressed with their equipment which was in fact ordered for the *Galloway Princess*. We were particularly impressed with the higher pressure/ low diameter pipework which was extremely good.

We had long discussions on disposal of sewage for this ship. Proposals were many and varied and were, in order of preference (1) a sewage treatment plant similar to earlier ships, (2) a vacuum system with retention tanks for pumping out at sea, (3) a vacuum system with facilities for pumping the retained sewage into the shore system when in port, (4) maceration, chlorination and pumped directly overboard. Option 4 was discarded after listening to the pleas of the local fisherman while Option 3 was discarded when the local authority confirmed that a concentrated load being pumped over a short period could not be accommodated into the shore system. Option 2 was discarded as the ship was never more than nine miles from shore and no opportunity was available to pump overboard. Therefore, option 1 was followed quite successfully.

While the *Galloway Princess* was building, there was an international reassessment of the capacity of lifeboats and all had to be remeasured. We carried out the official remeasurement at Harland & Wolff's one Saturday morning using shipyard workers, all kitted out with lifejackets. To our consternation, the new 150 person boats were reduced to 112 and the smaller boats had similar reductions. We then had to fit additional liferafts and davits at extra stations to make up the difference.

We coined the phrase of "LSA (life saving appliance) Length," that being the space along the ship's side available to fit lifeboats and/ or rafts, between the aft side of the bridge wings and a point defined as 1.5 boat lengths forward of the propellers. As a last note, the ship was 10 months late.

The vessel serves today as the *Stena Galloway*.

1980 ST. ANSELM
1981 ST. CHRISTOPHER

These two ships were virtual repeats of the *Galloway Princess* but with some significant differences. First, the speed required was a knot higher than the 'Galloway' and higher powered main engines were fitted. Secondly a bow rudder was required for the Dover service. Thirdly larger bow thrusters were required by the operators to ensure rapid turnround and good manoeuvrability in port.

An interesting series of experiments was carried out during the trials of the *St. Anselm* and *St. Christopher*. Steering trials were carried out using bow thrusters only at both ahead and astern speeds. The norm had been that with ships having a bow rudder, used only when going astern, the bow thrusters lost effective side thrust at about 4 knots which is when the bow rudder became effective. The thrusters on the 'Saints' were able to maintain and alter a course up to 7 knots both ahead and astern.

On these ships the deck machinery was supplied by Norwinch who provided the same random use of capstans and winches with a ring main but at lower pressure and large diameter piping.

Bill Henderson was Shipping Services Manager in Dover when these ships were designed and he stated that in the turnround time in Dover, he could only allow ten minutes clear for loading all necessary shop, duty free, bar and catering stores. This clearly was a problem in that there was no side quay or cranage for any stores access alongside the ship.

We therefore arranged large stores alongside the upper vehicle deck with wide, flush coaming, fire doors so that trains of special stores trolleys could be run up the upper ramp into the ship and

St Anselm (Mike Louagie)

directly into the stores, with 'empties' being taken out by the same prime mover on its return trip.

We achieved it, but when you can see the whole of the two large vehicle decks completely cleared of traffic in 8 minutes, as we have done, you wonder why the panic.

Again both ships were 10 months late and we lost a whole summer season of high capacity traffic.

The vessels are still in service, the 'Anselm' serving as the *Stena Cambria* while the 'Christopher' is the *Stena Antrim*.

1981   ST. DAVID

The fourth of the series was originally ordered as a Fishguard ship but as the *Stena Normandica* had proved successful on the route to Rosslare, the *St. David* was earmarked for Holyhead. A stern bridge was added and public rooms

modified but the vehicle arrangements etc. remained the same.

Steve Dickman suffered his second main engine catastrophe on this ship. During the test bed trials in the works, one of the main engines was restarted after a break, the governors failed to stop the engine and it ran up speed to destruction.

One significant change on this ship was that in an attempt to limit the weight growth, the builders proposed, and we accepted, that they should fit a vacuum sewage system. An Evac system was fitted with the resulting saving in weight by the use of very much smaller bore pipework.

On each of the four ships the cargo access equipment was supplied by MacGregor's and a notable feature of this was the action of the doors to the upper vehicle space which were guillotine type – 6 metres high and 8 metres wide.

St David (Miles Cowsill)

On trials with the *St. David* off the mouth of Belfast Lough, and for some distance up and down the Irish Sea, we were unaware that we had been the subject of a silent target practice by a U.K. nuclear submarine until the ship was called up by the sub's Captain. He had gratefully accepted a target that like all ships on trials, moved erratically, first ahead, then astern, then quick, slow, turning both ways, ideal for his crew training.

The ship was 10 months late and today serves as the *Stena Caledonia*.

1983   ST. CATHERINE and ST. HELEN

These were a real departure for the I.O.W. service being larger, more powerful, faster, and, with much better port facilities at each end of the route, able to meet growing demand on the Portsmouth/ Fishbourne service.

Although totally double-ended in loading and discharging Tony decided that on this generation, the speed required necessitated unidirectional motion at sea and the propulsion was arranged with two Voith Schneider units aft and one forward, all of the largest practicable size. The engine rooms on these craft, at 108 feet long, were the longest in a U.K. merchant ship and the configuration was made possible by the U shaped cofferdam tanks built at the sides and continuing underneath the machinery space to obviate flooding of the engine room in the event of grounding damage. Thus all the machinery could be in one space. Continuing Sealink's policy of safety, we fitted a one-shot open drencher system over the main units of machinery to be used as a first attack on any outbreak of fire before the main Halon system was activated and the whole place evacuated.

On these ships we moved back, at last, to a fully enclosed bridge and this was strongly welcomed by the navigating officers.

The cargo access equipment was supplied by MacGregor's but we had a few teething problems with the hoistable car deck panels. We had insisted that the construction had to be as light as possible to enable maximum clear heights to be achieved and this led to some distortion in the panels which proved difficult to eliminate.

The ships were extremely manoeuvrable and on trials with a not quite standing start and using all three Voith units we managed a full 360 degree swing in 58 seconds – surely a record for a ship capable of carrying 1,000 passengers.

1986   ST. CECILIA
1990   ST. FAITH

These were two repeats of the *St. Catherine* although they were built at Cochrane's of Selby rather than Robb's in Leith, which had closed following completion of the *St Helen*.

CONVERSIONS

1955   ST. PATRICK and ST. DAVID

These conversions, carried out in Falmouth, involved the modernisation of passenger and crew spaces concurrent with the fitting of a Matther and Platt sprinkler system in the accommodation and service spaces. On those ships, as with others of the older ones, the accommodation for stewards was in an open multi-berth compartment.

1964   ST. DAVID

This ship was converted to a single level car carrier with side loading doors which gave access to a shore-based ramp leading to the old cattle walkway tunnel which was only suitable without difficulty for small and medium sized cars. The loading and discharging could be frequently interrupted by the ranging of the ship at the quay in rough weather. Some crew spaces were removed and rebuilt elsewhere clear of the new car deck.

The greater part of the new car deck had been a cargo and mail hold. Hatches in the main deck needed to be sealed petrol tight, the sprinkler system extended, water spray curtains fitted, ventilation to car deck standards fitted while pipework, routing of electrical cables, telegraph connections were all moved. Stairways and access doors to machinery and other spaces were rebuilt to A-Class standards.

This was one occasion that we fitted A0 fire resisting shutters and found to our consternation that these shutters were so finely balanced on the magnetic hold-back latches that the normal ship's vibration soon made them operate without warning. The first intimation was a thundering bang as the shutter came rattling down and hit the deck.

At the same time, the structural fire protection within the accommodation and service space was updated with fire doors and shutters fitted in many places.

1964   FALAISE

This was another conversion of a classic passenger ship to a single level car carrier, this time with stern access to the shore bridge. Similar work to that on *St. David* was carried out but with additional work, and extensive modifications to public spaces.

Originally a Southampton-based vessel, in June 1964 the ship introduced a vehicle ferry service between Newhaven/Dieppe. With the *Senlac* in service, the *Falaise* was moved to Weymouth to initiate the vehicle carrying service to the Channel Isles.

After conversion, two bow rudder damages, caused by contact with the Newhaven piers, led to the demotion of one master and a severe reprimand to another. Captain "Mac" Collier on appointment as the Southern Region's Marine Superintendent investigated and found that there had also been a number of near misses when the *Falaise* had inexplicably sheered to one side. Tony advised "Mac" that the symptoms were consistent with directional instability, ie inability to steer a required course. British Ship Research Association were called in to advise and carry out tests at sea. As a result, modest increases to the rudder area and to deadwood aft resolved the problem, moreover the Masters were held blameless and their disciplinary penalties revoked. (A number of eminent naval architects are of the view that the *Herald of Free Enterprise* capsize was initiated by a similar directional stability phenomenon.)

During the conversion of the *Falaise*, for the first time we fitted straight line window wipers made by Wynstruments that Don had seen at the recent Boat Show and intended for small ships. These were a vast improvement on the type fitted on other ferries and had great advantages over the clear-view screens. We have continued fitting them on every ship since.

Falaise (Jim Ashby collection)

1964   NORMANNIA

A conversion similar in scope and intent to the *Falaise* with the ship moving base from Southampton to Dover.

While carrying out the conversion work it was discovered that the 1/4 inch to a foot scale 'as fitted' general arrangement plans supplied by Denny's, and which we had been closely working to, gave the breadth of the main passenger deck at the bridge front as about 8 inches too wide on each side, and this entailed the loss of some seats in the newly designed forward lounge.

An incident occurred some years later when the ship caught the underwater remains of a 'lost' stone stair at the Admiralty Pier in Dover and holed the side shell in way of the main turbine room. She was shifted quickly into the Tidal Basin where she was expected to settle safely but water seeped into the tunnel spaces in ever increasing amounts through what were thought to be watertight cable glands and she almost sank at the berth. It was an expensive salvage exercise.

An interesting side issue to the conversion was that the staff relations were so poor in the old Marine Department of the Southern Region that when the ship left Southampton to go to the shipyard for conversion, the officers and crew had not been informed officially that the majority of them would be required to move to Dover area when the ship returned from the yard three months later.

On completion of the *Normannia* conversion at Hawthorn Leslie's, a cocktail party was held in the forward bar to thank the shipyard employees for their timely completion. The legendary Captain John Hume, master of the ship and well known for his dry sense of humour, in conversation with Tony commented, 'I believe you are building a Deeeesel ferry in this yard', and on this being confirmed he responded, 'I have no desire to be propelled across the Channel by a series of explosions.' Economies had however sounded the death knell of the steam turbine which had served ferries so well for so many years.

1965   HIBERNIA and CAMBRIA

At the time, the *Hibernia* and *Cambria* had the largest passenger capacity of any U.K. ships but needed a total refurbishment of the passenger spaces. We stripped out to bare steel in some spaces, back only to the panelling in others, refitted the galley and pantries and refurbished the crew accommodation. The structural fire protection was updated at the same time with steel bulkhead insulation and the fitting of fire doors and shutters in many places.

1967   SOUTHSEA, BRADING and SHANKLIN

These Portsmouth/ Ryde Isle of Wight ferries were built by Denny's in 1948 (*Shanklin* in 1951) and were sadly in need of refurbishment in the passenger service spaces. We did not, unfortunately have the resources to restore them to their original state and catering needs for the service dictated most of what we did but it was very interesting exercise on an older generation of ships. An upper Spar Deck for 170 passengers was also fitted.

Of the three ships only the *Southsea* remains and is, at the time of writing, laid-up at Newhaven.

Designing Ships for Sealink

1967   DUKE OF ROTHESAY

The *St. David* had initiated the car carrying service from Fishguard to Rosslare but soon ran out of capacity and it was decided to move the *Duke of Rothesay* from Heysham, convert her to a single level car carrier and rebase her at Fishguard.

Crew accommodation at the aft end, passenger cabins in the midship area and cargo spaces aft and forward of the superstructure were cleared to make the clear vehicle space. The large casings of a steam ship left large obstructions in the centre but sufficient space was available port and starboard for two lines of cars abreast the casings.

We retained the use of the cattle walkways in the quay at Fishguard and a new type of hydraulically operated side sliding steel weathertight door designed and supplied by MacGregor's had its first application in this conversion and proved very successful. The passenger certificate was reduced from 1,800 to 1,400.

When we examined the tenders for the conversion of the *Duke of Rothesay*, Cammell Laird Repair Yard were the lowest by a wide margin and they were the first we asked to meet us. They arrived for a 10.00 meeting and apologised for having to withdraw their price. They had realised they had missed out the cost of the joiner work labour. We asked them then to tell us that cost and to withdraw while we considered the position. We were able to tell them when they returned that subject to our discussions on the other aspects, which were in fact OK, that they still would get the job. Relief all round and we got a good conversion.

1968   BOLTON ABBEY and MELROSE ABBEY

As an almost optimistic gesture, the two ships had a 52 feet section inserted into their cargo space to attempt to make the Hull – Rotterdam service viable but they did not survive in service much longer.

1969   ISLE OF ELY

Following the successful introduction of the 'Sea Freightliners,' the *Isle of Ely* had her container holds converted to a cellular system to be able to carry I.S.O. containers loaded by the same cranes used by the 'Sea Freightliners.'

1969   COLCHESTER

A similar conversion to the Isle of Ely but made more worthwhile by lengthening the container holds by 54 feet.

1970   DUKE OF LANCASTER and
DUKE OF ARGYLL

These conversions were, in many ways, similar to that carried out on the *Duke of Rothesay* but more extensive modifications were made. On these ships a stern door for access to

the shore bridge was fitted and this necessitated the moving of the steering gear to a new flat below deck and the re-routeing of the emergency steering gear rods round the new stern aperture.

We also took the opportunity to remove the original side sliding hatch covers in the well decks forward and aft together with the associated shell doors. These had been an interesting innovation in 1956 and consisted of side sliding concertina type hatch covers attached to a hinging section of deck that connected on to the side shell doors that opened outwards to enable cargo and mails to be craned in at high tide in Belfast through the ships' sides as the transporter cranes had not enough height to traverse cargo over the bulwarks. This was a very difficult structural arrangement that worked very well commercially.

When the after accommodation block was modified, space was arranged on the centreline to accept two coaches loaded by the stern door and reversed down the shore bridge on to the ship.

Regulations were changing as more became clear from studies of intermediate flooding, and so on these two ships we fitted what we believe were the first example of watertight doors to limit the extent of flooding in the event of damage. The doors were hydraulically operated and jack-knifed up into the deckhead, designed to our requirements, and supplied by MacGregor. Sealink unknowingly had notched up another 'first'.

1976   CALEDONIAN PRINCESS

With the 'Caley P.' now on the Weymouth – Channel Isles route, we had to find room for an extra 300 'inside' seats to provide a greater degree of passenger comfort. The only area where this could be done was at the aft end of the Boat Deck. We added new enclosed spaces to the existing house, but the profile became much less attractive. Access to the new space was not very good and it was not one of those projects that we looked on with pride. In this case, expediency took precedence over beauty.

Similar extensions were added to the *Antrim Princess* and *Ailsa Princess* at Stranraer and these were quickly christened 'Sanderson's Sheds' after John Sanderson, the manager of the Larne route.

1976   AVALON

It was with regret that we converted the *Avalon* for vehicle carrying service between Fishguard and Rosslare. She was a beautiful looking ship but with the necessary additions of deckhouses forward and aft, her profile was spoilt for ever.

The *Avalon* was converted to a car carrier with a small mezzanine deck at the after end and with stern door access to new shore bridges in Fishguard and Rosslare. Flood control doors,

Above: **Earl Godwin**
(FotoFlite)
Below: **Ailsa Princess**
(Miles Cowsill)

Earl Leofric (FotoFlite)

similar to those on the 'Dukes,' were also added during the conversion. Accommodation on the main deck consisted mainly of passenger cabins which were lost in the conversion as were the deluxe and special cabins on the boat deck where the space was required for crew accommodation. Refurbishment of public spaces plus addition of spaces forward and aft took place and the ship became a popular ferry at Fishguard leaving at intervals to help out at Holyhead.

1976   EARL LEOFRIC
(ex. HOLYHEAD FERRY I)

This was a major conversion to substantially increase the Ro-Ro capacity of the ship, and not primarily to increase car capacity, and entailed the removal of the fixed mezzanine deck from aft of midships to the forward end, the provision of portable mezzanine decks for a greater area and the fitting of a bow visor and inner bow door. The latter modifications entailed a considerable amount of work on the forward mooring deck to clear space for a visor and to rearrange mooring equipment.

To enable heavier axle loads to be carried in the former car only areas of the main deck, it was decided to fit doubler plates to the whole area but these proved troublesome as the flexing of the deck under load tended to fracture the plug welds.

We had the task of stripping-out the asbestos insulation throughout the passenger and crew spaces as work was to be done in virtually every space during the conversion. The ship was in Smith Dock at North Shields and the yard was virtually at a standstill for a time as the specialist

removal personnel and the chemists moved in. Asbestos was then a very dirty word and total precautions were taken. After the stripping-out and the ship being certified clean, work advanced rapidly and an excellent conversion took place. Public spaces and crew accommodation areas were rebuilt, extended and refurbished. The number of passengers was reduced from 1,000 to 725 and the car capacity increased from 153 to 205.

1977   EARL SIWARD (ex. DOVER)

This was a similar conversion to the *Earl Leofric* but a larger modification to the main deck was carried out where we removed deck plating, doubled the beams and laid new, thicker, plating to accept the heavier axle loads.

Another big difference was that , as in other Continental yards, little notice was taken of the dangers of asbestos. All Sealink personnel were banned from the ship until it had been certified clean by the B.R. Chemist.

With the modifications to the 'Leofric' and 'Siward' we saw the last butcher's shops disappear. Meat had been delivered to these and earlier ships in large pieces such as hind quarters, hung in the cold store and cut to requirements. By this time the catering departments were buying cut portions and economising on both staff, storage and waste.

The passenger certificate was reduced from 1,000 to 680 but cars only increased from 203 to 209.

The ship is today a floating night-club below the Tyne Bridge at Gateshead.

SHIPS BOUGHT OR CHARTERED

John Hendy

1970 ULIDIA

This was the first of many deals with Stena Line. The ship was taken over before completion and supervised in the final stages by Sealink personnel for the Stranraer service to Larne. This was a new type of ship for us, being predominately Ro-Ro with a small passenger complement of 36. Stern access was modified for Stranraer service.

Stabilisers were fitted in the ship during the conversion. These were bought second hand from Brown Bros. although never fitted to a ship, and were redundant from a bankrupt project in Yugoslavia. The price was reduced from £150K to £75K.

1971 DALRIADA

Another Stena ship chartered for Stranraer to cater for the increasing Ro-Ro traffic.

1972 ANDERIDA

The *Anderida* was bought as a stopgap for the Dover/ Dunkerque rail ferry service as the *Saint Eloi* was still fitting-out and the *Shepperton Ferry* was life expired. Rail tracks were fitted to the main deck, the stern was modified to accept the heavy shore bridges and the stern door adapted to the new position.

An amazing incident took place in Dunkerque when an enthusiastic train driver ran a rake of wagons too quickly on to the ship, rammed the forward buffers with enough impact to break the moorings and the ship broke free from the berth. One rail wagon fell into the water between the ship and the terminal. Stabilisers were fitted on a similar basis to the *Ulidia*.

1976 EARL GODWIN

The *Earl Godwin*, still under her original name of *Svea Drott,* was chartered at short notice in 1975 to take over from the *Falaise* which had to be taken out of the Channel Isles service when her boilers were seen to be beyond economic repair. After completing the summer service, the decision was taken to buy the ship and a team of five of us with two Department of Transport surveyors did a thorough survey in Elsinore dry-dock. As a result of this survey work was put in hand, initially in Parkeston Quay, where a start was made on the main engines, and then in Holyhead where the major work was undertaken to bring the ship under the U.K. flag.

The ship had father and son engines port and starboard driving two controllable pitched propellers and the engines were totally rebuilt for the new service. The machinery spaces were thoroughly cleaned and we had never seen such dirty engine rooms as when we took over.

The majority of the outfitting was carried out by Holyhead workshops supervised by the H.Q. team and took eight months. An excellent job was done by the Holyhead team. On the *Earl Godwin* it was necessary, to meet DOT

Earl Godwin (FotoFlite)

St Anselm *(FotoFlite)*

Above: **Stena Caledonia**
(Miles Cowsill)
Below: **Stena Hibernia**
(Miles Cowsill)

Earl William (Miles Cowsill)

Regulations, to fit a second bow door as the original door was too far forward to be considered as a continuation of the collision bulkhead.

A proper weathertight seal between the visor and shell was fitted.

Part of the conversion work included re-routeing escapes for passengers from the lower decks, sealing off holes left in watertight bulkheads behind panelling and re-routeing pipework.

Ferry Publications Library

1977   DARNIA

This was one of six ships ordered by Stena from a shipyard on the Danube in Austria. She was completed as the *Stena Topper* in Romania and initially taken on charter from Fisher's.

She was the first Sealink ship with drive-through at the upper vehicle deck level and modifications were carried out in Harland's to raise the position of the visor in the open position. Stabilisers were also fitted in Belfast. Two further conversions took place in the ship and on both occasions the passenger accommodation was extended and the passenger complement increased.

1978   EARL WILLIAM

This vessel was built as the *Viking II* in

Norway during 1964 for Thoresen's new service between Southampton and Le Havre/ Cherbourg. The *Earl William* was bought to augment the Channel Isles service and was based at Portsmouth. Modifications to the cargo access gear forward and aft were necessary to fit the shore terminals, passenger accommodation was refurbished and life saving appliances increased to cater for the larger number of passengers and to comply with IMO regulations.

An additional inner bow door was fitted to meet collision regulations.

Miles Cowsill

1979   STENA NORMANDICA / ST. BRENDAN

Originally chartered and later bought from Stena, this ship was a popular choice for Fishguard and rapid increases in traffic to Rosslare followed her introduction.

Modifications to her bow and stern access doors took place and later a side vehicle access door was fitted to enable speedier loading of cars in Fishguard via a new ramp built on the quay.

Two further conversions were made involving extensions and modifications to the passenger accommodation.

A popular pastime introduced on board was clay pigeon shooting from a position over the stern.

1980 MANX VIKING

Bought from the consortium lead by Geoff Duke this ship had been built in Spain as the *Monte Castillo* for service in Spanish waters before her arrival on the service between Douglas and Heysham for the Manx Line.

Don's first sight of the ship was when we carried out a pre-purchase survey in Heysham. He went down below in a white boiler suit and came back orange coloured from rust from the double bottom and deep tanks although the rust was actually superficial.

After the purchase we carried out considerable modifications to the cargo access equipment with additional hoistable car decks being fitted.

We also extended and refurbished the passenger accommodation by adding a new shop complex. A new bulkhead was built across the engine room to obviate a possible deficiency in some intermediate flooding conditions.

During the survey at Heysham, the ship was arrested and an Admiralty writ was stuck to the mast for non-payment of former debts. The situation was resolved later that day.

1981 EARL GRANVILLE

Another Scandinavian ship bought to augment the Channel Isles service was Viking Line's *Viking 4*, the new ship being based at Portsmouth while the *Earl William* moved to her new base at Weymouth replacing the *Caledonian Princess*.

Renamed *Earl Granville*, an additional inner bow door was fitted to meet IMO requirements and the collision regulations.

Passenger accommodation was also extended and refurbished.

While the ship was being undocked from the floating dock owned by Seebeckwerft in Bremerhaven, water ballast had been incorrectly positioned and the ship gave a lurch as she started to lift from the blocks. A colleague was in a double bottom tank at the time and made a rapid exit.

Looking round the public spaces on the *Earl Granville* while preparing the specification for modifications, Don was asked by some stewards, who were sitting in the restaurant having a cup of tea before passengers came on board, whether he could include in the work the securing of wobbly table tops in that restaurant. He got under one of the tables had a look at the securing of the top to the base and suggested that if they drank less tea and used a screwdriver for five minutes, the table tops would not wobble. They had the good grace to admit that he was right and that if the table was in any of their homes they would have done it automatically. There have been many such instances but we must also point out there have been at least an equal number where crew members have made repairs and improvements with no other thought than making it a little bit more their ship.

FotoFlite

1981 SPEEDLINK VANGUARD

Chartered from Stena to run as a train ferry between Harwich and Zeebrugge, it was necessary to fit rail tracks on the main deck and these also had to be run on the surface of the Ro-Ro lift at the forward end. Modifications were made to the stern door to enable it to lift vertically at the rail terminal and a set of railway type signals were positioned along the train deck.

Manx Viking (Ferry Publications Library)

Above: **St Christopher**
(John Hendy)
Below: **St Faith**
(John Hendy)

Miles Cowsill

1982   ST. NICHOLAS

Originally ordered in Gothenburg by Sessan Line, the ship stood idle and unwanted for some months after Stena bought out their rivals Sessan. However work started again when Sealink showed an interest in chartering for the Harwich/ Hook route.

Additional cabins were fitted while some minor modifications were made to the cargo access equipment and the ship was put in service under the U.K. Flag still owned by a U.K. division of Stena.

The ship was later bought by Sealink and further modifications were made to public rooms, shops and catering outlets. The ship has a magnificent entertainment centre in the lounge aft with multi-level seating, bar, stage and dance floor. She is presently (1996) on the Southampton/ Cherbourg route sailing as *Stena Normandy*.

An odd item on this ship was that when the DOT examined the ship's side windows in way of embarkation positions they found that the fire resistant glass had been fitted the wrong way round and was arranged to resist a fire from outside rather than protect the life saving appliances from a fire inside. These were reversed at the first survey.

1985   EARL WILLIAM and EARL GRANVILLE

The two ships were sent to Aalborg in the winter of 1984/ 85 to have the passenger accommodation up rated to a very high standard for the projected Star Liner and Bateau-de-Luxe services to the Channel Isles.

Cabins were stripped-out and replaced with modern high quality standard cabins all with private facilities and the catering service areas and outlets stripped and rebuilt.

When that service closed the *Earl William* had a short spell at Harwich as a prison ship before embarking on a short-stint on the Liverpool – Dun Laoghaire service.

1990   FANTASIA and FIESTA

These two ships have had a chequered career. Built in Sweden for Swedish Owners in Baltic service they were sold to the Bulgarian nationalised transport authority and ran between Trieste, Patras and Syria occasionally calling at

Brindisi on the northern leg.

The ships were built as heavy Ro – Ro carriers with accommodation for 177 drivers, all with cabin berths and one public space containing dining room, bar, shop and lounge.

The third ship in the series, *Zenobia*, sank off Cyprus some years ago.

Sea Containers bought the ships for Sealink service but it was some time before the route was decided. Proposals for Harwich/ Hook, Fishguard/ Rosslare, Newhaven/ Dieppe were all examined before it was decided to run on Dover/ Calais. Among proposals investigated were 1,600 and 1,200 passengers all with cabin berths, 2,200 passengers with about 2/3 in cabin berths, 1,000, 1,200, 1,400, and 1,800 on day service with no cabin berths. Eventually the overall design was agreed and tenders invited for the work. Competition was keen and the project teetered between Germany, Italy and Spain before final proposals from Lloyd Werft in Bremerhaven clinched the order.

The ships were built to carry Ro-Ro on the tank top, accessed by a one vehicle lift, hydraulically operated, on the main deck accessed directly from the shore by a massive double hinged stern door and on the upper deck, open at the aft end, and accessed by a single fixed ramp from the main deck. The ship was wide enough for most vehicles, particularly for articulated trucks to be able to turn within the beam while the stern-only access was sufficient for the longer routes where most of a day would be available for port operations.

On Dover/ Calais it was essential to have double-ended loading and discharge and bow access was a firm requirement in the specification.

The clear height between the main and upper decks and between upper and the main passenger deck was enough to allow ISO containers to be loaded two-high on low-loaders but this was not required for Sealink services. With the requirement for a massive increase in space for passengers, we looked at various proposals including raising the superstructure to fit an additional complete deck extending into the area above the open upper vehicle deck. Eventually it was decided to leave the superstructure more or

Channel Seaway *(FotoFlite)*

less intact, and actually lower the upper vehicle deck within the total vehicle space, to recover the unwanted clear height.

The upper vehicle deck was cut free level with the face of the heavy frames and lowered in situ to leave 5 metres clearance above the main deck.

About 900 tonnes of steel were cut and lowered in three main sections and secured in place in the new position level with an additional shell stringer.

This allowed space above the lowered vehicle deck to fit an additional complete steel deck still leaving 5 metres clear height for vehicles in the upper space. The worst aspect for the shipyard in this movement of the upper vehicle deck was that we required large deck to deck windows in the new public spaces created on the new passenger deck, and the realignment of piping services along the ship's sides to ensure these were clear of the new windows was extremely difficult. To make this possible we designed special offset linings over the deep ship's side frames to accommodate vertical piping runs.

The new deck was extended right to the aft end and the upper vehicle space almost completely enclosed, leaving only a small area at the aft end open at the sides for the carriage of some categories of dangerous goods.

On the *Fantasia* and *Fiesta*, the "LSA Length" (see *Galloway Princess*) was greatly reduced by the twin funnels and so a novel solution had to be found.

The sponsons saved the day as we were able to bring passengers down both inside and outside stairs and use inflatable slides from them to the liferaft boarding platforms. Without this shortening of the inflatable slides we would not have been able to carry the required number of passengers.

The davits for lowering the boats were also specially designed for these two ships, having to swing the boats 2 metres clear of the side of the deck to be able to embark passengers from the sponsons.

During the winter/ spring of 1984/ 85 we actually co-operated with twelve different interior design architects all engaged in different aspects of the updating of the fleet during the refit period. None had previously worked on ships.

That was obviously too large a number and in subsequent years only three or four architectural practices were involved.

In 1989 we had another major change when Warren Platner, the American Architect who had prepared the interior and exterior designs for Sea Containers House, was appointed Interior Design Architect for the major conversions of the *Fantasia* and *Fiesta*. Warren Platner had not worked on a project in a shipyard before and Don found it a great experience to be project manager for two ships built in Sweden, as cargo Ro-Ro ships with passenger capability of 177 to be converted in Germany for a U.K. company owned by an American, Mr. James Sherwood, with an American interior design architect. You can see the great results when you cross on the ships between Dover and Calais.

A cartoon involving lorry drivers was shown casually by Don to Warren Platner while schemes were being planned for the decorative treatment of the ships and Warren immediately took this up, researched his subject and procured a highly amusing set of cartoons to decorate the Ro-Ro drivers' lounges on each ship. They proved to be a very popular addition to the spaces and were a good conversation starter.

Fantasia and *Fiesta* (FotoFlite)

PROJECTS NOT COMPLETED

Many ideas, some of which involved considerable research and technical effort, never saw the light of day. At least the multitudinous designs for a Dover/ Dunkerque train ferry, the first of which was done in 1958, eventually saw fruition in 1968 in the *Vortigern*, known in Dover initially as the 'Forty Gins.'

Ideas never progressing beyond the drawing board stage included over the years :-

Stretching Dover's 'Saint' class vessels – One that comes to mind was the project to lengthen the *St. Anselm* and *St. Christopher*. We had got to the stage of producing a new general arrangement, machinery arrangement, arrangement of additional public rooms and crew accommodation, specifications for the work (hull, machinery, electrical and decorative contract) and had all necessary copies run off and ready to be issued with invitations to tender before the project was stopped. There were numerous other lengthening proposals e.g the *Saint Eloi* and the *St. Edmund* and there was even a plan to shorten the *Cambridge Ferry* to allow a better fit in Dover's Train Ferry Dock.

Dover/ Dunkerque Train Ferry – Hart Fenton commenced detailed design work on a new train ferry for Dover – Dunkerque, keeping our colleagues in French Sealink fully informed. Finally negotiations between Sea Containers and British Rail were broken off and our ship was not built. The design work was not wasted however as with some further modifications the ship was eventually built as the S.N.C.F. ferry, *Nord Pas-de-Calais*.

Parkeston Quay – Zeebrugge Train Ferry – There was also the double deck train ferry project to run from a new two level train loading berth up river from Parkeston Quay to a new berth in Zeebrugge. This again was an exciting project for all concerned but the eventual costs loaded on by the rail works killed it off.

New Humber Ferries – Designs were drawn out for new Humber ferries but were overtaken by the decision to commence the Humber Bridge.

New Isle of Wight Ferries – At one time there were plans to ship all Portsmouth – Isle of Wight traffic through Ryde by introducing passenger/ car

Sealink SWATH project

ferries onto the route. More plans to construct new shallow draught ferries (currently stymied by local objections) or to lengthen the three existing ferries for the Lymington/ Yarmouth service have also been mooted.

The SWATH Project – SWATH train ferries for Harwich/ Zeebrugge, an unfulfilled revolutionary design.

SWATH ferries were also intended to replace the Dover-based Hovercraft and extend high speed services throughout the Irish and Continental routes.

Of these the two SWATH (Small Waterplane Area Twin Hulls) were, technically, the most interesting. The two projects were quite different in concept, although the advantages of the excellent sea-keeping characteristics of SWATH design were common to both – passengers would not be seasick, wagons would not be in danger of being derailed.

The sketch of the train ferry proposal indicated the three draft idea which would have allowed simple shore terminal arrangements to be combined with an economic and sea-kindly open water draft. The greatly increased capacity of these ferries was a means of providing a rail service to the Continent capable of competing economically with road vehicle traffic via either Ro-Ro ferries or the potential Channel Tunnel.

In the months before privatisation, much research was undertaken into the design of a fast SWATH passenger/ car ferry, suitable for service around the coast of the UK. Tank tests were carried out at the Vicker's St. Albans model basin, and gave encouraging results. Design sketches show the General Arrangement and Cross section of the proposal. The main hull including vehicle deck was to be constructed in high tensile steel with aluminium superstructures. Propulsion was to be by conventional high speed diesel engines, mounted at vehicle deck level, with geared drives to

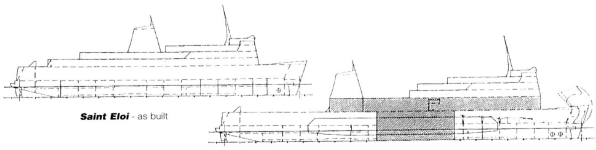

Saint Eloi - as built

Saint Eloi - lengthening project

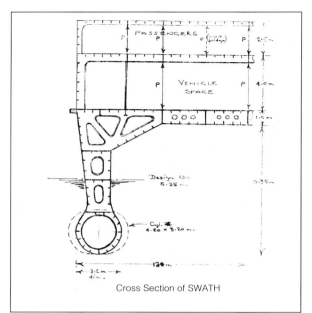

Cross Section of SWATH

propellers/water jets. The main advantages claimed for this design were speed and comfort on passage, also flexibility of service provided by smaller, faster, and transferable units.

After privatisation, the SWATH fast ferry project was dropped, and investment in wave piercing catamarans preferred. These craft had the advantages of being both faster and less costly, albeit with inferior comfort in bad weather. Perhaps in Sealink we were a few years too early in pushing the fast craft concept. There is no doubt that the post-privatisation Sealink/ Sea Containers initiative in investing in the first high speed passenger/ vehicle craft has spearheaded a world-wide explosion in the field. It is of interest that these early 'wave-piercing' catamarans were of identical capacity to the 'handy size' SWATH envisaged in 1982/3, however traffic growth now justifies investment in much larger units.

Tug-Barge Systems – In the course of the all-embracing operational research exercise which preceded investment in the Harwich/ Zeebrugge and Holyhead/ Dublin/ Belfast cellular container ships, tug-barge systems were investigated as an alternative to conventional ships. Larry Gloston, an American naval architect, proposed a configuration in which a tug could be mechanically linked to a container barge. The system was thoroughly tank tested at the model basin in Wageningen, Holland. Economically the tug-barge system was found to be superior to the conventional ship, however reliability of service considerations (a first essential always for Sealink routes) over-ruled its adoption. Larry Gloston's 'Sea-Link' did however live on until 1995 in the 'Sealink' corporate identity, which he agreed could be adopted by the British Rail Shipping and International Services Division and its Continental partners.

THE SHIP/SHORE INTERFACE

Our great-grandfathers were the originators of what is now known as a 'through-transport' system. Passengers could rely on the rail system to provide

ferries linking Great Britain with Ireland and the Continent, taking advantage of fully integrated timetables.

The advent of roll-on/ roll-off vehicular traffic, originally in the form of train ferries (Harwich/ Zeebrugge) later supplemented by carriage of cars in addition to wagons (Dover/ Dunkerque) and then pure road vehicles (*Princess Victoria/ Lord Warden* onwards) established a base from which Ro-Ro traffic developed in the post war years. There were misgivings in the railway dominated Sealink organisation about the encouragement of commercial vehicle traffic to the detriment of potential rail ferry business, however these doubts were abandoned in the mid-60's when the design of drive-through ferries with space for high vehicles throughout their length became the norm.

The ship/ shore interface for Ro – Ro ferries in the 1950's was logically determined by a need for interchangeabilty of ships between specialised rail and road services, hence the adherence to a rounded stern shape (to fit the Dover and Dunkerque terminals) and the adoption of a system in which the shore connecting 'link-span' bridge was landed on the deck of the ferry. Scandinavian ferry services, with negligible tidal variations, adopted a simpler system in which the connecting ship/ shore ramps were carried on the ferry. This led to many problems of incompatibility when Continental ferries were bought or chartered.

As new Ro – Ro services were introduced, sometimes with existing or converted ferries and sometimes with new buildings, close co-operation to meet our ship-fit and tidal criteria was essential between naval architects and the civil engineers responsible for terminal engineering. New terminal facilities sprouted at Stranraer, Larne, Heysham, Belfast, Holyhead, Dun Laoghaire, Fishguard, Rosslare, Portsmouth, Fishbourne, Lymington, Yarmouth, Newhaven, Dieppe, Dover, Calais, Folkestone, Boulogne, Dunkerque, Ostende, Harwich, and Hook of Holland. All involved consultation and close co-operation with the shore link designers to ensure compatibility of ship and terminal and also to ensure maximum flexibility of ferries between services, and to permit accommodation of chartered ferries designed for different terminal geometries. Perhaps the most unusual design involved the utilisation of the old cattle ramps under the quays at Fishguard and Rosslare to provide side access for cars to the *St. David* when converted. The most difficult nut to crack was the conversion of the *Essex Ferry* and *Norfolk Ferry* to fit the Harwich and Dunkerque rail terminals, the squarer ends of the Harwich ferries being cut back about 2 metres at the widest point to fit in the Dunkerque piles intended for rounder sterns. This conversion had, some years previously, been pronounced impracticable but was successful, albeit requiring a 'shoe-horn' fit at the French end.

NOTABLE FIRSTS

First with inflatable liferafts in pods on ramps.

First with davit launched liferafts.

Late with marine escape chutes although we started investigations and Don did the first drawings in 1958, but we left it until the *Fantasia* before we were convinced the problems had been largely ironed out.

First with fire doors without coamings.

90% of accidents reported on Sealink ships involved coamings.

First with mezzanine car decks.

First with sprinklers 1935.

First with mulsi-spray 1956

First with drenchers 1967

First with U.K. cellular container ship.

First ferry to be fitted with stabilisers – the *Isle of Sark* in 1936.

ASSISTING THE NATIONAL MARITIME MUSEUM

A letter sent out by the late Frank Carr, Director, at the time, of the National Maritime Museum in Greenwich, to many U.K. shipowners was received by Leslie Harrington in the early 1960s.

The letter suggested that any surplus items of memorabilia of ships could be handed to the museum instead of the usual home of many items, the dust bin.

Leslie Harrington instructed Don to write to all the Regional marine headquarters departments and the ports with a copy of Mr. Carr's letter and requested that anything that could be spared should be sent via our office to Greenwich. We started with a flood. We had tea chests, crates, hessian sacks, large parcels, small parcels, all full of plans, specifications, photographs, old catalogues. It seem that everyone had entered into the spirit of this and had a good clear out.

Periodically the ports were asked again and the flow of items would start once more. Don has made a few trips to Greenwich with the car boot full.

The majority of B.R. and previous rail company records were deposited with the Railway Archivist until that office was absorbed into the National Records Office but we obtained official dispensation to donate all "ship" items to Greenwich, the commercial, legal and other items still going to the National Records Office. This allowed Greenwich to reproduce drawings of older ships for students, enthusiasts etc. without infringing copyright.

One important item donated to the National Maritime Museum was the carved wooden decorative outer skin of one of the paddle boxes from the *Lucy Ashton*. The piece was semicircular and about 10 feet long.

FOLKESTONE MEMORIES

What appeared to be a harebrained scheme to begin with was seriously considered some years ago. We had a problem with the bow thrust unit on the *Dover* and we investigated drying out the ship on the hard sand on the NE side of the harbour at Folkestone. The sand was surveyed and found clear of rocks or other loose debris but it was eventually called off and a diver carried out a temporary repair.

Tony is quite proud of the fact that when we had two of our Folkestone ships beached neither suffered heavy bottom damage.

At the end of an overnight crossing from Folkestone, the *Vortigern* grounded at the entrance to Ostend and when the tide fell she was suspended with the bow on an outfall and the stern on the beach before refloating.

The *Hengist* was blown out of Folkestone in a violent storm and was beached sideways on under the cliffs to the north of Folkestone harbour.

When the *Vortigern* incident occurred our M.D. Len Merryweather jokingly suggested we should call out Red Adair.

We investigated some years ago a scheme for a second arm to partly enclose Folkestone harbour and give protection to the berths from east and north east winds. The proposal was to purchase a redundant tanker or bulk-carrier of about 20,000 gross tons, berth it at a maximum tide in the required position and then allow it to settle in and silt up. The upper works would have been removed together with all accommodation and machinery items, the interior filled with dredged material and left to form an eventual barrier to wind and waves. The connection to the shore at the near end would have been made with normal civil engineering methods.

It was soon accepted by the proposers that it was not really a viable proposition for Folkestone.

IRISH SEA PLEASURES

One of the old-fashioned pleasures of visiting Holyhead , years ago, was having lunch on the Mail Boat. The Port Manager, on my earliest visits Capt. Ardern, later Capt. Lord, invited the visiting surveyors from Lloyd's and the Board of Trade, plus any of the more senior staff from London, to lunch. As many of you will know, the ship that arrived at the incoming berth at 00.15, stayed in port all day, moving over to the departure berth during the morning ready for the evening sailing. At the Captain's invitation we gathered in the Ladies' Lounge on either the *Cambria* or *Hibernia*, and waited for 'The Box' to appear. This was a polished wooden box containing the bottles, and we were all allowed a snifter before lunch. Lunch was served in the first-class restaurant, and was always good.

Another Holyhead custom was catching the sleeper back to London, not bad when you arrived on the ship from Dun Laoghaire, but meant a tedious wait in the port if you were returning after a normal day's meetings that finished too late to catch the afternoon train. The pubs closed at 22.00, the restaurants were used to customers going home early and the station buffet took on a new look after about 23.00 : dreary. The sleeper left Holyhead at 01.00.

We used sleepers a lot. They were an excellent

time-saver, work late at the office and take the sleeper to Glasgow, Stranraer, Fishguard, or wherever, to enable an early start the following day. Sleepers also helped to keep us solvent. In those days the rate of expenses meant that Don had 27/6d for twenty four hours. When you deducted about 22/6d for bed & breakfast we had very little left to pay for meals, and no legal way of claiming for more. When a sleeper was taken we had to deduct one pound from our allowance, but that usually saved us 2/6d which was very welcome. The deduction of one pound went on for years, and meant even bigger savings in later years.

On the Stranraer route in 1954 was the *Princess Margaret*, built in 1931, and a 'good' sea boat. Don's first few trips between Stranraer and Larne were a bit rough and he was amused to find that the 'roughness' gauge on the route was which furniture skidded across the forward lounge, from corner to corner when the ship rolled. When the *Princess Maud* came up from Holyhead for survey relief all calculations of roughness disappeared, the 'Maud' was reputed to be able to roll on damp grass.

When the three 'Dukes' were built, it was decided that we should be able to survey the stabilisers in the dry dock at Holyhead but the dock was much too narrow to be able to extend them. It was then agreed we should build a recess in the dock wall at each side coinciding with the positions of the fins and large enough to be able to work on the fins when extended. When the civil engineers worked out the costs, the usual horror was expressed, the size of the recesses reduced and despite what we said about being able to cope with a range of fin positions in other future ships, the Railway accountancy procedure which limits the spread of costs on to the one project effectively stopped all but the minimum of work on the idea. When the costs were again produced we went ahead, built the recesses and had about 2 feet working space round the fins, which meant accurate docking for the ships to be able to extend the fins safely.

Soon after we fitted the hinged type on the *Caledonian Princess* and the recesses were outdated.

CONCLUSION

The sad thing about designing ships is that they, like their designers have finite lives. The majority of the ferries we have designed have now been either consigned to the breakers yard or are in their twilight years in foreign waters. One notable exception is the *Tern* on Lake Windermere, built in 1891. No ! we did not design her but were responsible for the design of her successful centenary rebuild.

Privatisation was traumatic but the authors and their team worked happily for 10 years with a new and extended family in Hart Fenton, a Sea Containers subsidiary, during which time Sealink work continued until the take-over by Stena who were old friends for many years.

Post-privatisation, expected investment in major

Ro-Ro fleet units never materialised, except for the trend-setting conversions of the *Fantasia* and *Fiesta*. The upgrading of the passenger areas of the existing Sealink fleet was more of an agony than an ecstasy, however involvement in high-speed ferries was exhilarating.

Tragedy (*Herald of Free Enterprise* and *Estonia*) has tempered the pride we both have in the development of the Ro-Ro multi-purpose passenger ferry type, in which we have played a leading role. Safety of life at sea has always been the prime consideration in our designs, indeed demanded by our principals. It is unfortunate that the most successful, not only surviving but thriving, area of the dwindling U.K. merchant fleet has been blighted by these tragedies. We are confident that there is young blood prepared to take up the challenge of recent draconian legislation to find design solutions to meet the demands of the critics who seem to be determined to encourage the builders of tunnels to the detriment of our maritime heritage.

APPENDIX

NEW SHIPS LIST

Abbreviations:
H.B. Hopper Barge
P.F. Passenger Ferry
P.V.F. Passenger & Vehicle Ferry
M.P.V. Multi-Purpose Vessel
T.F. Train Ferry
Con. Containers
P.C. Passenger/ Cargo
Car/Cat Car and Cattle Carrier

Year/Name Port Type Builder

1950
LAGA II Heysham H.B. Ferguson

1956
DUKE OF LANCASTER Heysham/Belfast P.F. Harland & Wolff
DUKE OF ARGYLL Heysham/Belfast P.F. Harland & Wolff
DUKE OF ROTHESAY Heysham/Belfast P.F. Denny

1957
GLEN SANNOX Ardrossan/Arran P.V.F. Ailsa
BARDIC FERRY Preston/Larne P.V.F. Denny
ESSEX FERRY Harwich/Zeebrugge T.F. Brown
LOCHALSH Isle of Skye P.V.F. Ailsa

1958
IONIC FERRY Preston/Larne P.V.F Denny
CONTAINER ENTERPRISE Heysham/Belfast Con. Ailsa
CONTAINER VENTURER Heysham/Belfast Con. Ailsa
BOLTON ABBEY Hull/Rotterdam P.C. Brooke Marine
DARLINGTON Goole/Continent Cargo Lamont
WAKEFIELD Goole/Continent Cargo Lamont
ISLE OF ELY Harwich/Rotterdam Cargo Goole

1959
MAID OF KENT Dover/Boulogne P.V.F. Denny

MELROSE ABBEY Hull/Rotterdam P.C. Brooke Marine
HARROGATE Goole/Continent Cargo Lamont
SELBY Goole/Continent Cargo Lamont
YORK Goole/Continent Cargo Inglis
LEEDS Goole/Continent Cargo Inglis
ELK Soton/Ch.Isles Cargo Brooke Marine
MOOSE Soton/Ch.Isles Cargo Brooke Marine
COLCHESTER Harwich/Rotterdam Cargo Goole
MEECHING Newhaven Tug Harris
FRESHWATER Lymington/Yarmouth P.V.F. Ailsa

1960
KYLEAKIN Isle of Skye P.V.F. Ailsa
SLIEVE DONARD Holyhead/Dublin Car/Cat Ailsa
RED NAB Heysham H.B. Ailsa
CAESAREA Weymouth/Ch.Isles P.F. J.S. White

1961
CERDIC FERRY Tilbury/Antwerp P.V.F. Ailsa
SARNIA Weymouth/Ch.Isles P.F. J.S. White
FISHBOURNE Portsm'th/Fishbourne P.V.F. Philips
CAMBER QUEEN Portsm'th/Fishbourne P.V.F. Philips
CATHERINE Tilbury/Gravesend P.F. White
EDITH Tilbury/Gravesend P.F White
ROSE Tilbury/Gravesend P.F. White
CALEDONIAN PRINCESS Stranraer/Larne P.V.F. Denny

1962
DORIC FERRY Tilbury/Antwerp P.V.F. Ailsa

1963
AVALON Harwich/Hook P.F Stephen
CAMBRIDGE FERRY Harwich/Zeebrugge T.F. Hawthorn

1964
GAELIC FERRY Tilbury/Antwerp P.V.F. Ailsa

1965
HOLYHEAD FERRY I Holyhead/Dun L. P.V.F. Hawthorn
DOVER Dover/Boulogne P.V.F. Swan Hunter
PORTREE Isle of Skye P.V.F. Lamont

1967
BROADFORD Isle of Skye P.V.F. Lamont
ANTRIM PRINCESS Stranraer/Larne P.V.F. Hawthorn

1968
ST. GEORGE Harwich/Hook P.V.F. Swan Hunter
SEA FREIGHTLINER I Harwich/Zeebrugge Cont. Redhead
SEA FREIGHTLINER II Harwich/Zeebrugge Cont. Redhead

1969
VORTIGERN Dover/Dunkirk M.P.V. Swan Hunter
CUTHRED Portsm'th/Fishbourne P.V.F. Richards

1970
BRIAN BOROIME Holyhead/Dublin Cont. Verolme Cork
RHODRI MAWR Holyhead/Dublin Cont. Verolme Cork

1971
AILSA PRINCESS Stranraer/Larne P.V.F. Breda, Italy

1972
HENGIST Folkestone/Boulogne P.V.F. Brest, France
HORSA Folkestone/Boulogne P.V.F. Brest, France

1973
SENLAC Newhaven/Dieppe P.V.F. Brest, France
ST. EDMUND Harwich/Hook P.V.F. Cammell Laird
CAEDMON Portsm'th/Fishbourne P.V.F. Robb Caledon
CENWULF Lymington-Yarmouth P.V.F. Robb Caledon
CENRED Lymington-Yarmouth P.V.F. Robb Caledon

1975
SAINT ELOI Dover/Dunkirk M.P.V. P.Ligure, Genoa

1977
ST. COLUMBA Holyhead/Dun L. P.V.F. Aalborg

1980
GALLOWAY PRINCESS Stranraer/Larne P.V.F. Harland & Wolff
ST. ANSELM Dover/Calais P.V.F. Harland & Wolff

1981
ST. CHRISTOPHER Dover/Calais P.V.F. Harland & Wolff
ST. DAVID Holyhead/Dun L. P.V.F. Harland & Wolff

1983
ST. CATHERINE Portsm'th/Fishbourne P.V.F. Robb
ST. HELEN Portsm'th/Fishbourne P.V.F. Robb

1986
ST. CECILIA Portsm'th/Fishbourne P.V.F Cochrane

1990
ST. FAITH Portsm'th/Fishbourne P.V.F Cochrane

CONVERSION OF B.R. OWN SHIPS

1955
ST. PATRICK & ST. DAVID Fishguard
Modernisation of passenger & crew spaces & fitting of sprinklers in accommodation and service spaces.

1964
ST. DAVID Fishguard
Converted to single deck car carrier (66 cars)
FALAISE Newhaven (ex. Southampton) Converted to car carrier (96 cars)
NORMANNIA Dover (ex. Southampton)
Converted to car carrier (111 cars)
HIBERNIA & CAMBRIA Holyhead
Modernisation of passenger spaces.

1967
DUKE OF ROTHESAY Fishguard (ex. Heysham)
Converted to car carrier (111 cars).
BOLTON ABBEY & MELROSE ABBEY (1968) Hull
Cargo spaces lengthened by 52 feet.

1969
ISLE OF ELY Parkeston Quay
Conversion of container holds to cellular arrangement.

1969
COLCHESTER Parkeston Quay
Conversion of container holds to cellular
arrangement and lengthening by 54 feet.

1970
DUKE OF LANCASTER & DUKE OF ARGYLL
Heysham
Conversion to car carriers (105 cars).
SOUTHSEA BRADING & SHANKLIN Portsmouth
Modernisation of passenger spaces.

1976
CALEDONIAN PRINCESS Weymouth (ex. Fishguard
& Stranraer) Modification of passenger spaces,
construction of an extended deckhouse and addition
of 300 more 'inside' seats to make the vessel more
compatible for the Channel Islands route.
AVALON Fishguard (ex. Parkeston Quay)
Conversion to car carrier (198 cars).
EARL LEOFRIC (ex. HOLYHEAD FERRY I) Dover
(ex. Holyhead) Conversion to through loader.

1977
EARL SIWARD (ex. DOVER) Dover
as EARL LEOFRIC

SHIPS BOUGHT OR CHARTERED AND MODIFIED FOR A PARTICULAR ROUTE

1970
ULIDIA Stranraer. Cargo access modified and public
spaces extended.

1971
DALRIADA Stranraer as ULIDIA

1972
ANDERIDA Dover
Cargo access modified and rail tracks fitted on main deck.

1976
EARL GODWIN Weymouth
Cargo access and Mezzanine decks modified,
passenger spaces up-dated.

1977
DARNIA Stranraer
Cargo access modified, passenger spaces extended.

1978
EARL WILLIAM Portsmouth
Cargo acceess modified, passenger spaces extended.

1979
STENA NORMANDICA Fishguard
Cargo access modified, passenger spaces extended
and refurbished.

1980
MANX VIKING Heysham.
Cargo access modified, passenger spaces modernised.

1981
EARL GRANVILLE Portsmouth
Cargo acceess modified, passenger spaces extended.
SPEEDLINK VANGUARD Stern access modified and
rail tracks laid on main and upper decks.

1982
ST. NICHOLAS Modified for Harwich-Hook service.

1983
EARL GRANVILLE & EARL WILLIAM Extensively
modified for the Channel Isles services.

1990
FANTASIA & FIESTA Extensive modifications for
Dover-Calais service.

Vortigern and *Hengist* (FotoFlite)